Georgia Coach, GPS Edition, Standards-Based Instruction, Mathematics 2

Coach™

America's Best for Student Success®

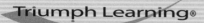

Triumph Learning®

Georgia Coach, GPS Edition, Standards-Based Instruction, Mathematics 2
109GA
ISBN-10: 1-60471-629-0
ISBN-13: 978-1-60471-629-0

Written by: Colleen O'Donnell Oppenzato
Cover Image: The peach is the state fruit of Georgia. © IT Stock Free/JupiterImages.

Triumph Learning® 136 Madison Avenue, 7th Floor, New York, NY 10016

Table of Contents

Georgia Performance Standards Mathematics 2

Letter to the Student

Dear Student,

Welcome to *Coach*! This book provides instruction and practice that will help you master all the important skills you need, and gives you practice answering the kinds of questions you will see on your state's test.

The *Coach* book is organized into chapters and lessons. Each of the lessons has three parts. The first part walks you through the skill so you know just what it is and what it means. The second part gives you a model, or example, with hints to help your thinking about the skill. And the third part of the lesson gives you practice with the skill to see how well you understand it.

We wish you lots of success this year, and hope the *Coach* will be a part of it!

Test-Taking Checklist

Here are some tips to keep in mind when taking a test. Take a deep breath. You'll be fine!

✓ Follow the directions! Remember, you won't get points if you don't do what the directions say!

✓ If you're having trouble understanding a question, try to reword it. How else can the question be asked?

✓ On questions you're not sure about, eliminate all answers that you are positive are incorrect. Then choose the answer that seems right.

✓ Really stumped? Skip the question and come back to it later.

✓ Be extra aware of words that are **bolded**, *italicized*, or <u>underlined</u>. They are usually important.

✓ Graphs and charts contain important information. Illustrations often provide clues.

✓ If you're allowed, use scrap paper. Take notes or make sketches to help you answer questions.

✓ Read all the answer choices before picking the best answer. Sometimes more than one answer may be true. Your job is to choose the best answer.

✓ Make sure you've marked your answer correctly.

✓ If you finish early, read over your answers to check for mistakes. But don't get too caught up in changing your answers—your initial answer is usually correct.

✓ Spend a reasonable amount of time on each question. Don't rush through, but make sure to keep up your pace, too. You don't want to run out of time.

Good Luck!

Georgia Performance Standards Correlation Chart

GPS	Georgia Performance Standard	Coach Lesson(s)
Number and Operations Students will use the complex number system.		
MM2N1. Students will represent and operate with complex numbers.		
MM2N1.a	Write square roots of negative numbers in imaginary form.	1
MM2N1.b	Write complex numbers in the form $a + bi$.	1
MM2N1.c	Add, subtract, multiply, and divide complex numbers.	1, 2, 3
MM2N1.d	Simplify expressions involving complex numbers.	1, 2, 3

GPS	Georgia Performance Standard	Coach Lesson(s)
Algebra Students will investigate piecewise, exponential, and quadratic functions, using numerical, analytical, and graphical approaches, focusing on the use of these functions in problem-solving situations. Students will solve equations and inequalities and explore inverses of functions.		
MM2A1. Students will investigate step and piecewise functions, including greatest integer and absolute value functions.		
MM2A1.a	Write absolute value functions as piecewise functions.	5
MM2A1.b	Investigate and explain characteristics of a variety of piecewise functions including domain, range, vertex, axis of symmetry, zeros, intercepts, extrema, points of discontinuity, intervals over which the function is constant, intervals of increase and decrease, and rates of change.	6
MM2A1.c	Solve absolute value equations and inequalities analytically, graphically, and by using appropriate technology.	7, 8
MM2A2. Students will explore exponential functions.		
MM2A2.a	Extend properties of exponents to include all integer exponents.	4
MM2A2.b	Investigate and explain characteristics of exponential functions, including domain and range, asymptotes, zeros, intercepts, intervals of increase and decrease, rates of change, and end behavior.	10
MM2A2.c	Graph functions as transformations of $f(x) = a^x$.	13
MM2A2.d	Solve simple exponential equations and inequalities analytically, graphically, and by using appropriate technology.	11, 12
MM2A2.e	Understand and use basic exponential functions as models of real phenomena.	9
MM2A2.f	Understand and recognize geometric sequences as exponential functions with domains that are whole numbers.	14
MM2A2.g	Interpret the constant ratio in a geometric sequence as the base of the associated exponential function.	14
MM2A3. Students will analyze quadratic functions in the forms $f(x) = ax^2 + bx + c$ and $f(x) = a(x - h)^2 + k$.		
MM2A3.a	Convert between standard and vertex form.	15
MM2A3.b	Graph quadratic functions as transformations of the function $f(x) = x^2$.	16

MM2A3.c	Investigate and explain characteristics of quadratic functions, including domain, range, vertex, axis of symmetry, zeros, intercepts, extrema, intervals of increase and decrease, and rates of change.	15
MM2A3.d	Explore arithmetic series and various ways of computing their sums.	17
MM2A3.e	Explore sequences of partial sums of arithmetic series as examples of quadratic functions.	17
MM2A4. Students will solve quadratic equations and inequalities in one variable.		
MM2A4.a	Solve equations graphically using appropriate technology.	18
MM2A4.b	Find real and complex solutions of equations by factoring, taking square roots, and applying the quadratic formula.	19
MM2A4.c	Analyze the nature of roots using technology and using the discriminant.	18, 19
MM2A4.d	Solve quadratic inequalities both graphically and algebraically, and describe the solutions using linear inequalities.	20
MM2A5. Students will explore inverses of functions.		
MM2A5.a	Discuss the characteristics of functions and their inverses, including one-to-oneness, domain, and range.	22
MM2A5.b	Determine inverses of linear, quadratic, and power functions and functions of the form $f(x) = \frac{a}{x}$, including the use of restricted domains.	21
MM2A5.c	Explore the graphs of functions and their inverses.	21, 22
MM2A5.d	Use composition to verify that functions are inverses of each other.	23

GPS	Georgia Performance Standard	*Coach* Lesson(s)
Geometry Students will explore right triangles and right-triangle trigonometry. They will understand and apply properties of circles and spheres, and use them in determining related measures.		
MM2G1. Students will identify and use special right triangles.		
MM2G1.a	Determine the lengths of sides of 30°-60°-90° triangles.	24
MM2G1.b	Determine the lengths of sides of 45°-45°-90° triangles.	24
MM2G2. Students will define and apply sine, cosine, and tangent ratios to right triangles.		
MM2G2.a	Discover the relationship of the trigonometric ratios for similar triangles.	25
MM2G2.b	Explain the relationship between the trigonometric ratios of complementary angles.	25
MM2G2.c	Solve application problems using the trigonometric ratios.	26
MM2G3. Students will understand the properties of circles.		
MM2G3.a	Understand and use properties of chords, tangents, and secants as an application of triangle similarity.	28
MM2G3.b	Understand and use properties of central, inscribed, and related angles.	27, 28
MM2G3.c	Use the properties of circles to solve problems involving the length of an arc and the area of a sector.	29
MM2G3.d	Justify measurements and relationships in circles using geometric and algebraic properties.	27, 28, 29

MM2G4. Students will find and compare the measures of spheres.		
MM2G4.a	Use and apply surface area and volume of a sphere.	30
MM2G4.b	Determine the effect on surface area and volume of changing the radius or diameter of a sphere.	31

GPS	Georgia Performance Standard	*Coach* Lesson(s)
Data Analysis and Probability Students will demonstrate understanding of data analysis by posing questions to be answered by collecting data. Students will organize, represent, investigate, interpret, and make inferences from data. They will use regression to analyze data and to make inferences.		
MM2D1. Using sample data, students will make informal inferences about population means and standard deviations.		
MM2D1.a	Pose a question and collect sample data from at least two different populations.	32
MM2D1.b	Understand and calculate the means and standard deviations of sets of data.	33
MM2D1.c	Use means and standard deviations to compare data sets.	33
MM2D1.d	Compare the means and standard deviations of random samples with the corresponding population parameters, including those population parameters for normal distributions. Observe that the different sample means vary from one sample to the next. Observe that the distribution of the sample means has less variability than the population distribution.	34
MM2D2. Students will determine an algebraic model to quantify the association between two quantitative variables.		
MM2D2.a	Gather and plot data that can be modeled with linear and quadratic functions.	35, 36, 37
MM2D2.b	Examine the issues of curve fitting by finding good linear fits to data using simple methods such as the median-median line and "eyeballing."	36
MM2D2.c	Understand and apply the processes of linear and quadratic regression for curve fitting using appropriate technology.	36, 37
MM2D2.d	Investigate issues that arise when using data to explore the relationship between two variables, including confusion between correlation and causation.	35

GPS	Georgia Performance Standard	*Coach* Lesson(s)
Process Standards The following process standards are essential to mastering each of the mathematics content standards. They emphasize critical dimensions of the mathematical proficiency that all students need.		
MM2P1. Students will solve problems (using appropriate technology).		
MM2P1.a	Build new mathematical knowledge through problem solving.	31
MM2P1.b	Solve problems that arise in mathematics and in other contexts.	9, 15
MM2P1.c	Apply and adapt a variety of appropriate strategies to solve problems.	7, 8, 11, 12, 18, 19, 20, 31, 33
MM2P1.d	Monitor and reflect on the process of mathematical problem solving.	12, 18, 19, 20
MM2P2. Students will reason and evaluate mathematical arguments.		
MM2P2.a	Recognize reasoning and proof as fundamental aspects of mathematics.	28
MM2P2.b	Make and investigate mathematical conjectures.	16, 28
MM2P2.c	Develop and evaluate mathematical arguments and proofs.	16, 28
MM2P2.d	Select and use various types of reasoning and methods of proof.	1, 23, 28
MM2P3. Students will communicate mathematically.		
MM2P3.a	Organize and consolidate their mathematical thinking through communication.	6, 10, 15, 22, 32
MM2P3.b	Communicate their mathematical thinking coherently and clearly to peers, teachers, and others.	16, 22, 32
MM2P3.c	Analyze and evaluate the mathematical thinking and strategies of others.	23, 28
MM2P3.d	Use the language of mathematics to express mathematical ideas precisely.	6, 10, 15
MM2P4. Students will make connections among mathematical ideas and to other disciplines.		
MM2P4.a	Recognize and use connections among mathematical ideas.	14, 17, 36, 37
MM2P4.b	Understand how mathematical ideas interconnect and build on one another to produce a coherent whole.	14, 17, 22, 29
MM2P4.c	Recognize and apply mathematics in contexts outside of mathematics.	9, 26, 29, 36, 37
MM2P5. Students will represent mathematics in multiple ways.		
MM2P5.a	Create and use representations to organize, record, and communicate mathematical ideas.	5, 21, 26
MM2P5.b	Select, apply, and translate among mathematical representations to solve problems.	5, 21, 26
MM2P5.c	Use representations to model and interpret physical, social, and mathematical phenomena.	5, 9, 21, 26

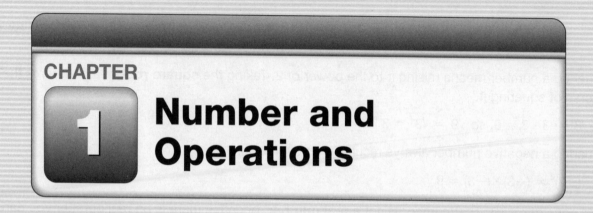

CHAPTER 1

Number and Operations

1 Introduction to Complex Numbers

MM2N1.a, MM2N1.b, MM2N1.c, MM2N1.d, MM2P2.d

Squaring a number means raising it to the power of 2. Taking the **square root** of a number is the inverse of squaring it.

$$3^2 = 3 \cdot 3 = 9, \text{ so } \sqrt{9} = \sqrt{3^2} = 3$$

Squaring a negative number always results in a positive number.

$$(-3)^2 = (-3) \cdot (-3) = 9$$

Now consider $\sqrt{-9}$. That number is not a **real number**, because there is no real number you can multiply by itself to get -9. However, we can represent $\sqrt{-9}$ as an **imaginary number**. Imaginary numbers are written with i, which is equal to $\sqrt{-1}$. By using the property that $\sqrt{ab} = \sqrt{a} \cdot \sqrt{b}$, you can write the square root of any negative number as the product of a real number and i. That is, you can write it in the form bi.

$$\sqrt{-9} = \sqrt{-1} \cdot \sqrt{9} = 3i$$

EXAMPLE 1

Write $\sqrt{-20}$ in imaginary form.

STRATEGY **Rewrite the square root in the form bi.**

STEP 1 Write $\sqrt{-20}$ as a product of b and i.
$$\sqrt{-20} = \sqrt{-1} \cdot \sqrt{20}$$

STEP 2 Simplify $\sqrt{20}$.
$$\sqrt{20} = \sqrt{4} \times \sqrt{5} = 2\sqrt{5}$$

STEP 3 Substitute and multiply.
$$\sqrt{-1} \cdot \sqrt{20} = i \cdot 2\sqrt{5} = 2i\sqrt{5}.$$

SOLUTION **In imaginary form, the number is written $2i\sqrt{5}$.**

You should also know how to find different **powers** of i. If you need to review properties of **exponents**, look ahead to Lesson 4.

$$\sqrt{-1} = i$$
$$i^2 = (\sqrt{-1})^2 = -1 \quad \longleftarrow \quad \text{The square of } i \text{ is equal to } -1.$$
$$i^3 = i^2 \cdot i^1 = -1 \cdot i = -i$$
$$i^4 = i^2 \cdot i^2 = -1 \cdot -1 = 1$$
$$i^5 = i^4 \cdot i^1 = 1 \cdot i = i$$
$$i^6 = i^5 \cdot i^1 = i \cdot i = i^2 = -1$$
$$i^7 = i^6 \cdot i^1 = -1 \cdot i = -i$$
$$i^8 = i^4 \cdot i^4 = -1 \cdot -1 = 1$$

When the exponent is a multiple of 4, the power of i is equal to 1.

Notice that the pattern repeats: i, -1, $-i$, 1. You can use this pattern to simplify large powers of i.

EXAMPLE 2

Simplify i^{35}.

STRATEGY   **Use the pattern of powers of i to find i^{35}.**

   STEP 1   Find the closest multiple of 4 that is not greater than the exponent, 35.
   32 is the closest multiple of 4. So, $i^{32} = 1$.

   STEP 2   Write i^{35} as the product of a multiple of 4 and another power of i. Simplify.
   $$i^{35} = i^{32} \cdot i^3 = 1 \cdot -i = -i$$

SOLUTION $i^{35} = -i$

A **complex number** has two parts: a real part and an imaginary part. It is written in the standard form $a + bi$, in which a and b are real numbers, a is the real part, and bi is the imaginary part.

EXAMPLE 3

Write $-3 + \sqrt{-7}$ as a complex number in standard form.

STRATEGY   **Identify the real part and the imaginary part. Then rewrite the imaginary part in the form bi.**

   STEP 1   Identify the real part and the imaginary part.

$$-3 + \sqrt{-7}$$

   real part   imaginary part

STEP 2 Rewrite the imaginary part in imaginary form.

$$\sqrt{-7} = \sqrt{-1} \cdot \sqrt{7} = i\sqrt{7}$$

STEP 3 Rewrite the number in the form $a + bi$.

$$-3 + \sqrt{-7} = -3 + i\sqrt{7}$$

SOLUTION **In standard form, the complex number is $-3 + i\sqrt{7}$.**

The absolute value of a complex number in standard form $a + bi$ is equal to $\sqrt{a^2 + b^2}$.

EXAMPLE 4

Find the absolute value of $-5 + 12i$.

STRATEGY **Identify a and b. Then find $\sqrt{a^2 + b^2}$.**

$a = -5$ and $b = 12$

$$\sqrt{a^2 + b^2} = \sqrt{(-5)^2 + 12^2} = \sqrt{25 + 144} = \sqrt{169} = 13$$

SOLUTION **The absolute value of $-5 + 12i$ is 13.**

COACHED EXAMPLE

Write $18 - \sqrt{-25}$ as a complex number in standard form.

THINKING IT THROUGH

Identify the real part and the imaginary part of the complex number.

The real part is _____. The imaginary part is _____.

Rewrite the imaginary part so it is in imaginary form. _____

Rewrite in the form $a + bi$.

$18 - \sqrt{-25} = $ _____ $-$ _____

The standard form is _____.

Lesson Practice

Choose the correct answer.

1. Which is equivalent to $\sqrt{-16}$?

   A. $i\sqrt{8}$

   B. $2i\sqrt{2}$

   C. $4i$

   D. $8i$

2. Which is equivalent to $\sqrt{-27}$?

   A. $-3i\sqrt{3}$

   B. $3i\sqrt{3}$

   C. $3i\sqrt{9}$

   D. $9i$

3. Which is equivalent to $\sqrt{-200}$?

   A. $10i\sqrt{2}$

   B. $20i$

   C. $100i$

   D. $100i\sqrt{2}$

4. Which is equivalent to i^{13}?

   A. 1

   B. i

   C. $-i$

   D. -1

5. Which is equivalent to i^{96}?

   A. 1

   B. i

   C. $-i$

   D. -1

6. What is the absolute value of $3 + 4i$?

   A. $\sqrt{5}$

   B. $\sqrt{7}$

   C. 5

   D. 7

7. Which shows the standard form of $70 + \sqrt{-3}$?

   A. $-3 + i\sqrt{70}$

   B. $-3 + 70i$

   C. $70 + i\sqrt{3}$

   D. $70 + 3i$

8. Which shows the standard form of $-1 - \sqrt{-64}$?

   A. $-9i$

   B. $-1 - 8i$

   C. $-1 + 8i$

   D. $9i$

9. What is the absolute value of $14 - 7i$?

   A. $7\sqrt{5}$

   C. $\sqrt{7}$

   B. $5\sqrt{7}$

   D. $\sqrt{5}$

10. Which shows the standard form of $-12 - \sqrt{-50}$?

    A. $-10 - 2i\sqrt{3}$

    B. $-12 - 2i\sqrt{5}$

    C. $-12 - 5i$

    D. $-12 - 5i\sqrt{2}$

2 Adding and Subtracting Complex Numbers

MM2N1.c, MM2N1.d

When you add **polynomials**, you group **like terms**.

$$(6 + 3x) + (4 + 2x) = (6 + 4) + (3x + 2x) = 10 + 5x$$

When adding complex numbers, you also group like terms. First, you group the real parts. Then you group the imaginary parts. Use the rules in the box below.

Addition	$(a + bi) + (c + di) = (a + c) + (b + d)i$
Subtraction	$(a + bi) - (c + di) = (a - c) + (b - d)i$

EXAMPLE 1

Find the sum: $(5 + 5i) + (3 - 7i)$

STRATEGY   Group the real parts. Group the imaginary parts. Then simplify.

STEP 1   Rewrite the problem without parentheses.

$$(5 + 5i) + (3 - 7i) = 5 + 5i + 3 - 7i$$

STEP 2   Group the real parts and the imaginary parts separately.

$$5 + 5i + 3 - 7i = (5 + 3) + (5i - 7i)$$

STEP 3   Simplify. Write the answer in standard form.

$$(5 + 3) + (5i - 7i) = 8 + (-2i) = 8 - 2i$$

SOLUTION   The sum is **$8 - 2i$**.

When subtracting, remember that: $-(a + bi) = (-1)(a) + (-1)(bi) = -a - bi$.

EXAMPLE 2

Find the difference: $(12 + 10i) - (3 + 10i)$

STRATEGY   **Group the real parts. Group the imaginary parts. Then simplify.**

STEP 1   Rewrite the problem without parentheses. Be sure to distribute the subtraction sign.

$(12 + 10i) - (3 + 10i) = 12 + 10i - 3 - 10i$

STEP 2   Group the real parts and the imaginary parts separately.

$12 + 10i - 3 - 10i = (12 - 3) + (10i - 10i)$

STEP 3   Simplify.

$(12 - 3) + (10i - 10i) = 9 + 0 = 9$

Note: $0i$ is the same as 0.

SOLUTION   **The difference is 9.**

You can also add or subtract imaginary numbers that are not in the imaginary form bi.

EXAMPLE 3

Find the sum: $\sqrt{-36} + \sqrt{-40}$

STRATEGY   **Write the terms in imaginary form. Then simplify.**

STEP 1   Write $\sqrt{-36}$ in imaginary form.

$\sqrt{-36} = \sqrt{-1} \cdot \sqrt{36} = i \cdot 6 = 6i$

STEP 2   Write $\sqrt{-40}$ in imaginary form.

$\sqrt{-40} = \sqrt{-1} \cdot \sqrt{40} = i \cdot 2\sqrt{10} = 2i\sqrt{10}$

STEP 3   Find the sum. Then factor out the greatest common factor.

The greatest common factor of $6i$ and $2i\sqrt{10}$ is $2i$.

$6i + 2i\sqrt{10} = 2i(3 + \sqrt{10})$

SOLUTION   **The sum is $2i(3 + \sqrt{10})$.**

COACHED EXAMPLE

Find the difference: $(3.5 + 7.8i) - (2.5 - 1.2i)$

THINKING IT THROUGH

Rewrite the problem without parentheses. Be sure to distribute the subtraction sign.

$(3.5 + 7.8i) - (2.5 - 1.2i) = $ _____

Group the real parts and the imaginary parts separately:

(_____ − _____) + (_____ + _____)

Simplify.

_____

In standard form, the difference is _____.

Lesson Practice

Choose the correct answer.

1. What is the sum?

   $$(2 + 7i) + (9 + 3i)$$

   A. $21i$

   B. $11 + 10i$

   C. $10 + 11i$

   D. $9 + 12i$

2. What is the difference?

   $$(11 + 7i) - (6 + i)$$

   A. $5 - 6i$

   B. $5 + 6i$

   C. $5 + 8i$

   D. $17 - 6i$

3. What is the difference?

   $$(12 + 8i) - (-3 - 10i)$$

   A. $9 - 18i$

   B. $9 + 2i$

   C. $15 - 2i$

   D. $15 + 18i$

4. What is the sum?

   $$(18 + 11i) + (-20 - 11i)$$

   A. -2

   B. $-2 - i$

   C. $-2 - 11i$

   D. $-2 - 22i$

5. Which is equivalent to
   $(4.6 + 0.4i) + (2.2 - 0.1i)$?

   A. $2.4 + 0.3i$

   B. $5 + 2.1i$

   C. $6.8 + 0.3i$

   D. $6.8 + 0.5i$

6. Which is equivalent to $\left(\frac{4}{9} - \frac{8}{9}i\right) - \left(\frac{5}{9} + \frac{1}{9}i\right)$?

   A. $-\frac{1}{9} - i$

   B. $-\frac{1}{9} - \frac{7}{9i}$

   C. $-1 - \frac{1}{9i}$

   D. $-1 - i$

7. Which is equivalent to $\sqrt{-24} - \sqrt{-54}$?

   A. $-3i\sqrt{30}$

   B. $-3i\sqrt{6}$

   C. $-i\sqrt{30}$

   D. $-i\sqrt{6}$

8. Which is equivalent to $\sqrt{-3} + \sqrt{-9}$?

   A. $-i - 3$

   B. $-i + 3$

   C. $i(\sqrt{3} + 3)$

   D. $i(\sqrt{3} - 3)$

Multiplying and Dividing Complex Numbers

MM2N1.c, MM2N1.d

The **distributive property** states that when a factor is multiplied by the sum of two terms, you can multiply each term by that factor and add the products.

$$a(b + c) = ab + ac$$

This property also applies to subtraction.

$$a(b - c) = ab - ac$$

You can use the distributive property to multiply complex numbers, but remember that you cannot leave i^2 in the final answer. Since $i^2 = -1$, use that fact to write the answer in standard form.

EXAMPLE 1

Find the product: $(3 - 5i)(6 + 2i)$

STRATEGY   Use the distributive property to multiply the two complex numbers.

STEP 1   Apply the distributive property.

Multiply 3, the first term in $(3 - 5i)$, by each term in $(6 + 2i)$.

Then, multiply $-5i$, the second term in $(3 - 5i)$, by each term in $(6 + 2i)$.

$$(3 - 5i)(6 + 2i) = (3 \cdot 6) + (3 \cdot 2i) + (-5i \cdot 6) + (-5i \cdot 2i)$$

STEP 2   Simplify. Remember to substitute -1 for i^2.

$$(3 \cdot 6) + (3 \cdot 2i) + (-5i \cdot 6) + (-5i \cdot 2i) = 18 + 6i - 30i - 10i^2$$
$$= 18 + 6i - 30i - 10(-1)$$
$$= 18 + 6i - 30i + 10$$

STEP 3   Add the products, combining the real parts and the imaginary parts separately.

$$18 + 6i - 30i + 10 = (18 + 10) + (6i - 30i) = 28 - 24i$$

Factor out the greatest common factor: $28 - 24i = 4(7 - 6i)$

SOLUTION   The product in standard form is $4(7 - 6i)$.

When you multiply two complex numbers in the forms $a + bi$ and $a - bi$, you are multiplying **complex conjugates**.

EXAMPLE 2

Find the product: $(7 + 4i)(7 - 4i)$

STRATEGY   **Use the distributive property to multiply the two complex numbers.**

STEP 1   Multiply both terms of the first number by each term of the second number.

$$(7 + 4i)(7 - 4i) = (7 \cdot 7) + [7 \cdot (-4i)] + (4i \cdot 7) + [4i \cdot (-4i)]$$

STEP 2   Add the products. Remember to substitute -1 for i^2 when you simplify.

$$(7 \cdot 7) + [7 \cdot (-4i)] + (4i \cdot 7) + [4i \cdot (-4i)] = 49 + -28i + 28i - 16i^2$$
$$= 49 + 0 - 16(-1)$$
$$= 49 + 16$$
$$= 65$$

SOLUTION   **The product is 65.**

The product of any **conjugate pair**, $a + bi$ and $a - bi$, is a real number.

$$(a + bi)(a - bi) = a^2 - b^2i^2 = a^2 + b^2$$

If there is an i in the denominator of a fraction, then it is not in standard form. However, if you multiply both the numerator and the denominator by the complex conjugate of the denominator, i will be eliminated from the denominator. Then you can write the quotient in standard form.

EXAMPLE 3

Write the fraction in standard form: $\frac{1 - 2i}{2 - 5i}$

STRATEGY   **Use complex conjugates.**

STEP 1   What is the complex conjugate of the denominator?

The complex conjugate of $2 - 5i$ is $2 + 5i$.

STEP 2   Multiply both the numerator and the denominator by that complex conjugate.

$$\frac{1 - 2i}{2 - 5i} \cdot \frac{2 + 5i}{2 + 5i} = \frac{(1 - 2i)(2 + 5i)}{(2 - 5i)(2 + 5i)}$$

$$= \frac{2 + 5i - 4i - 10i^2}{4 - 25i^2}$$

$$= \frac{2 + i - 10(-1)}{4 - 25(-1)}$$

$$= \frac{2 + i + 10}{4 + 25}$$

$$= \frac{12 + i}{29}$$

STEP 3   Rewrite the answer in the form $a + bi$.

$$\frac{12 + i}{29} = \frac{12}{29} + \frac{1}{29}i$$

SOLUTION   **The quotient in standard form is $\frac{12}{29} + \frac{1}{29}i$.**

Sometimes, you may need to write numbers in standard form before you multiply or divide them.

EXAMPLE 4

Write the fraction in standard form: $\frac{4\sqrt{3}}{-2 + \sqrt{-27}}$

STRATEGY   **Write the denominator in standard form. Then use complex conjugates.**

STEP 1   Write the denominator in standard form.

$$\sqrt{-27} = \sqrt{-1} \cdot \sqrt{27} = i \cdot 3\sqrt{3} = 3i\sqrt{3}$$

So, $-2 + \sqrt{-27} = -2 + 3i\sqrt{3}$

STEP 2   What is the complex conjugate of the new denominator?

The complex conjugate of $-2 + 3i\sqrt{3}$ is $-2 - 3i\sqrt{3}$.

STEP 3   Multiply both the numerator and the denominator by that complex conjugate.

$$\frac{4\sqrt{3}}{-2+3i\sqrt{3}} \cdot \frac{-2-3i\sqrt{3}}{-2-3i\sqrt{3}} = \frac{(4\sqrt{3})(-2-3i\sqrt{3})}{(-2+3i\sqrt{3})(-2-3i\sqrt{3})}$$

$$= \frac{-8\sqrt{3}-12i(\sqrt{3})^2}{4-9i^2(\sqrt{3})^2}$$

$$= \frac{-8\sqrt{3}-12i \cdot 3}{4-9 \cdot (-1) \cdot 3}$$

$$= \frac{-8\sqrt{3}-36i}{4-(-27)}$$

$$= \frac{-8\sqrt{3}-36i}{31}$$

STEP 4   Rewrite the answer in the form $a + bi$.

$$\frac{-8\sqrt{3}-36i}{31} = \frac{-8\sqrt{3}}{31} - \frac{36}{31}i = -\frac{8\sqrt{3}}{31} - 1\frac{5}{31}i$$

SOLUTION   The quotient in standard form is $-\frac{8\sqrt{3}}{31} - 1\frac{5}{31}i$.

COACHED EXAMPLE

Write the fraction in standard form: $\dfrac{3}{-2+i}$

THINKING IT THROUGH

The denominator is _____.

The complex conjugate of that denominator is _____ — _____.

Multiply both the numerator and denominator by that complex conjugate. Simplify.

$\dfrac{3}{-2+i} \cdot$ _____ = _____

= _____

= _____

= _____

Rewrite the answer in the form $a + bi$: _____

The quotient in standard form is _____.

Lesson Practice

Choose the correct answer.

1. Find the product: $(2 - 3i)(1 - 4i)$

 A. $-10 - 11i$

 B. $2 - 12i$

 C. $2 - 7i$

 D. $14 - 11i$

2. Write the fraction in standard form: $\frac{5}{1 + 2i}$

 A. $5(1 - i)$

 B. $5 + 2i$

 C. $1 - 2i$

 D. $1 - i$

3. Which is equivalent to $(8 + 5i)(8 - 5i)$?

 A. 39

 B. $64 - 25i$

 C. $64 + 25i$

 D. 89

4. Simplify: $\frac{2 - 4i}{4 + 3i}$

 A. $\frac{4}{25} - \frac{22}{25}i$

 B. $-\frac{4}{25} - \frac{22}{25}i$

 C. $-\frac{4}{25} - 22i$

 D. $-4 - \frac{22}{25}i$

5. Which is equivalent to $(5 - i\sqrt{10})(3 + i\sqrt{10})$?

 A. $5 + 2i$

 B. $15 + 2i$

 C. $25 + 2i$

 D. $25 + 2i\sqrt{10}$

6. Simplify: $\frac{-7 + 3i}{3 - i}$

 A. $-\frac{12}{5} - \frac{1}{5}i$

 B. $-\frac{12}{5} + \frac{1}{5}i$

 C. $-\frac{12}{5} + 5i$

 D. $-24 + \frac{1}{5}i$

7. Multiply: $\sqrt{-10} \cdot \sqrt{-24}$

 A. $12i\sqrt{10}$

 B. $4i\sqrt{15}$

 C. $-3\sqrt{15}$

 D. $-4\sqrt{15}$

8. Which is equivalent to $\frac{1 + \sqrt{-45}}{2 + \sqrt{-20}}$?

 A. $\frac{4}{3} + \frac{\sqrt{5}}{6}i$

 B. $\frac{4}{3} + \frac{5}{6}i$

 C. $\frac{4}{3} + i\sqrt{5}$

 D. $32 + 4i\sqrt{5}$

4 Properties of Exponents

MM2A2.a

Knowing how to work with exponents can help you multiply and divide imaginary numbers and complex numbers, as you did earlier in this chapter. It can also help you work with quadratic and exponential functions, like those that will appear in chapters 2 and 3.

An exponent shows how many times to use the base as a factor. If a is a real number and n is a positive integer, then

$$a^n = \overbrace{a \cdot a \cdot \ldots a}^{n \text{ times}}$$

For example, $4^3 = 4 \cdot 4 \cdot 4 = 64$.

The table below summarizes the properties of exponents.

Property	Examples
Product of Powers To multiply powers with the same base, add the exponents.	$a^m \cdot a^n = a^{m+n}$ $6^3 \cdot 6^2 = 6^{3+2} = 6^5 = 7{,}776$
Power of a Product Any product raised to an exponent is equal to each factor raised to that exponent.	$(ab)^n = a^n b^n$ $(2x)^3 = (2^3)(x^3) = 8x^3$
Quotient of Powers To divide powers with the same base, subtract the exponents.	$\dfrac{a^m}{a^n} = a^{m-n}$ $\dfrac{10^5}{10^3} = 10^{5-3} = 10^2 = 100$
Power of a Quotient When a fraction is raised to a power, the denominator and the numerator are each raised to that power.	$\left(\dfrac{a}{b}\right)^n = \dfrac{a^n}{b^n}$ $\left(\dfrac{2}{5}\right)^2 = \dfrac{2^2}{5^2} = \dfrac{4}{25}$
Power of a Power When a power is raised to another power, multiply the exponents.	$(a^m)^n = a^{mn}$ $\left(k^2\right)^4 = k^8$
Power of Zero Any nonzero value raised to the power of zero equals 1.	$a^0 = 1$ $11^0 = 1$
Negative Powers Any nonzero value raised to a negative power equals the **reciprocal** of that value with a positive exponent.	$a^{-n} = \dfrac{1}{a^n}$ $9^{-2} = \dfrac{1}{9^2} = \dfrac{1}{81}$

EXAMPLE 1

Simplify: $(-3p^5q^4)^2$

STRATEGY   **Use the rules of exponents.**

STEP 1   Which rule or rules will help you?

Power of a product: Any product raised to an exponent is equal to each factor raised to that exponent.

Power of a power: When a power is raised to another power, multiply the exponents.

STEP 2   Apply those rules.

Multiply the exponent of each factor by the exponent, 2.

$$(-3p^5q^4)^2 = (-3)^2 \cdot (p^{5 \cdot 2}) \cdot (q^{4 \cdot 2})$$
$$= 9p^{10}q^8$$

SOLUTION $(-3p^5q^4)^2 = 9p^{10}q^8$

EXAMPLE 2

Simplify: $7^{-2} \cdot (3b)^0$

STRATEGY   **Use the rules of exponents.**

STEP 1   Which rule or rules will help you?

Negative powers: Any value raised to a negative power equals the reciprocal of that value with a positive exponent.

Power of zero: Any value raised to the power of zero equals 1.

STEP 2   Find the value of the first factor.

$$7^{-2} = \frac{1}{7^2} = \frac{1}{49}$$

STEP 3   Find the value of the second factor.

$(3b)^0 = 1$, because the entire value $3b$ is raised to the power of 0.

STEP 4   Substitute and multiply.

$$7^{-2} \cdot (3b)^0 = \frac{1}{49} \cdot 1 = \frac{1}{49}$$

SOLUTION $7^{-2} \cdot (3b)^0 = \frac{1}{49}$

EXAMPLE 3

Simplify: $\dfrac{i^8}{i^3}$

STRATEGY   **Use the rules of exponents.**

STEP 1   Which rule or rules will help you?

Quotient of powers: To divide powers with the same base, subtract the exponents.

STEP 2   Apply that rule.

$$\frac{i^8}{i^3} = i^{8-3} = i^5$$

STEP 3   Use what you know about powers of i and multiplying powers with the same base to find the value of i^5.

Remember, if the exponent of i is a multiple of 4, its value is 1.

$$i^5 = i^4 \cdot i = 1 \cdot i = i$$

SOLUTION $\dfrac{i^8}{i^3} = i$

COACHED EXAMPLE

Simplify: $-5s^2t \cdot 3s^3t^6$

THINKING IT THROUGH

Product of powers: To multiply values with the same base, _____ the exponents.

Multiply the integers. Then use the exponent rule to multiply the variables.

$-5s^2t \cdot 3s^3t^6 =$ _____

The simplified value of $-5s^2t \cdot 3s^3t^6$ is _____.

Lesson Practice

Choose the correct answer.

1. The length of a rectangle is $6m^3$ units. Its width is $2m^2$ inches. What is its area?

   A. $8m^5$ in.^{2}

   B. $8m^6$ in.^{2}

   C. $12m^5$ in.^{2}

   D. $12m^6$ in.^{2}

2. Each side of a square is $3b^3$ centimeters long. What is the area of the square?

   A. $3b^5$ cm^2

   B. $3b^6$ cm^2

   C. $9b^5$ cm^2

   D. $9b^6$ cm^2

3. Which is equivalent to $\dfrac{25z^8}{5z^4}$?

   A. $5z^2$

   B. $5z^4$

   C. $20z^2$

   D. $20z^4$

4. Which is equivalent to $\left(\dfrac{6p}{q}\right)^3$?

   A. $\dfrac{18p^3}{q^3}$

   B. $\dfrac{216p}{q}$

   C. $\dfrac{216p^3}{q^3}$

   D. $\dfrac{216p^4}{q^4}$

5. Which is equivalent to $\dfrac{18r^{12}}{3r^2} \cdot r^0$?

   A. 0

   B. 6

   C. $6r^6$

   D. $6r^{10}$

6. Which is equivalent to $(5a^2bc^3)^3$?

   A. $125a^6b^3c^9$

   B. $125a^5b^3c^6$

   C. $5a^6b^3c^9$

   D. $5a^6bc^9$

7. Which is equivalent to $\dfrac{g^{-3}}{2h^{-4}}$?

   A. $\dfrac{2h^4}{g^3}$

   B. $\dfrac{h^4}{2g^3}$

   C. $\dfrac{h^4}{8g^3}$

   D. $\dfrac{h^3}{2g^4}$

1. Which is equivalent to $\sqrt{-72}$?

   A. $36i\sqrt{2}$

   B. $6i\sqrt{2}$

   C. $2i\sqrt{6}$

   D. $-36i$

2. Which is equivalent to $\frac{32k^9}{4k^3}$?

   A. $28k^6$

   B. $28k^3$

   C. $8k^6$

   D. $8k^3$

3. Which shows the standard form of $-5 - \sqrt{-81}$?

   A. $-14i$

   B. $-5 - 9i$

   C. $-5 - 9i\sqrt{3}$

   D. $4i$

4. What is the difference?

   $$(3 - i) - (-2 + 6i)$$

   A. $1 - 7i$

   B. $1 + 5i$

   C. $5 - 7i$

   D. $5(1 + i)$

5. What is the product?

   $$(4 - 3i)(7 + 2i)$$

   A. $34 + 13i$

   B. $34 - 13i$

   C. $22 + 13i$

   D. $22 - 13i$

6. Which is equivalent to $(8mn^3)^2$?

   A. $16mn^5$

   B. $64mn^6$

   C. $64m^2n^5$

   D. $64m^2n^6$

7. What is the sum?

   $$\left(\frac{3}{10} + \frac{9}{10}i\right) + \left(\frac{7}{10} - \frac{1}{10}i\right)$$

   A. $\frac{2}{5} + i$

   B. $\frac{2}{5} + \frac{4}{5}i$

   C. $1 - \frac{4}{5}i$

   D. $1 + \frac{4}{5}i$

8. Which is equivalent to $\frac{i^{10}}{i^2}$?

   A. 1

   B. i

   C. $-i$

   D. -1

9. What is the quotient?

$$\frac{-5 + i}{1 - 6i}$$

A. $\frac{11}{37} - \frac{29}{37}i$

B. $-\frac{1}{37} + \frac{29}{37}i$

C. $-\frac{11}{37} - \frac{29}{37}i$

D. $-1 + \frac{29}{37}i$

10. The length of a rectangle is a^2b^5 inches. Its width is ab^2 inches. What is its area?

A. ab^{10} square inches

B. a^2b^7 square inches

C. a^2b^{10} square inches

D. a^3b^7 square inches

11. Which is equivalent to $\sqrt{-60} - \sqrt{-15}$?

A. $i\sqrt{15}$

B. $i\sqrt{45}$

C. $2i\sqrt{15}$

D. $2\sqrt{15}$

12. Which is equivalent to $\frac{10r^{-7}}{s^{-5}}$?

A. $\frac{10s^5}{r^7}$

B. $\frac{10r^7}{s^5}$

C. $\frac{s^5}{10r^7}$

D. $\frac{10r^7}{10s^5}$

13. What is the absolute value of $7 - 24i$?

A. $\sqrt{31}$

B. $\sqrt{73}$

C. 17

D. 25

OPEN-ENDED QUESTION

14. Consider this complex number: $-6 + \sqrt{-4}$

   A. Write this complex number in standard form. Then write its complex conjugate in standard form.

      Standard form: _____

      Complex conjugate: _____

   B. Find the product of the two complex numbers in part A. Show your work.

   C. Consider this statement.

      The product of any two complex conjugates is always a real number.

      Is the statement true or false? Explain.

      _____

      _____

      _____

      _____

      _____

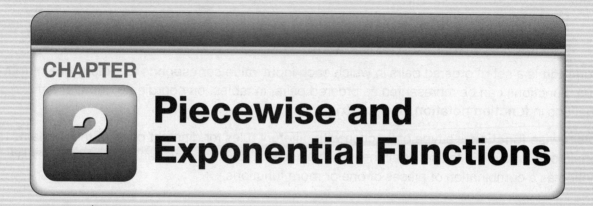

CHAPTER 2

Piecewise and Exponential Functions

5 Introduction to Piecewise Functions

MM2A1.a, MM2P5.a, MM2P5.b, MM2P5.c

A **function** is a set of ordered pairs in which each input value corresponds to exactly one output value. Functions can be represented as ordered pairs, in tables, on coordinate grids, or as equations in **function notation**, such as $f(x)$.

A **piecewise function** is a type of function with different rules for different parts of the **domain**. The domain of a function is the set of all the input values of a function. You can think of a piecewise function as a combination of pieces of one or more functions.

EXAMPLE 1

Graph the piecewise function $f(x) = \begin{cases} x - 4, & \text{if } x < 1 \\ 3x - 6, & \text{if } x \geq 1 \end{cases}$.

STRATEGY   Choose several input values in each domain and make tables of values. Then graph the points.

STEP 1   Choose input values to use in the table for the first piece of the function.

$x < 1$ means that the domain includes -2, -1, and 0. It does not include 1.

Include -2, 1, and 0 in your table. Also include 1 in parentheses. Even though 1 is *not* a possible value, finding the value of 1 helps you to see where to end the first piece of your graph.

STEP 2   Make a table of values and graph the first piece, $x - 4$, if $x < 1$.

x	f(x) = x − 4	f(x)
−2	$f(-2) = -2 - 4 = -6$	−6
−1	$f(-1) = -1 - 4 = -5$	−5
0	$f(0) = 0 - 4 = -4$	−4
(1)	$(f(1) = 1 - 4 = -3)$	(−3)

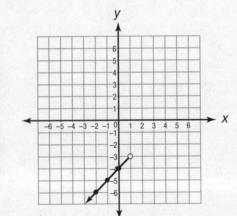

You put an open endpoint at $(1, -3)$ because 1 is *not* part of the domain for the first piece.

STEP 3   Choose input values for the table for the second piece, $3x - 6$, if $x \geq 1$.

   $x \geq 1$ means that the domain includes 1, 2, 3, and 4. Include those numbers in the table.

STEP 4   Make a table of values and graph the second piece.

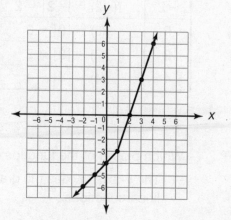

x	$f(x) = 3x - 6$	$f(x)$
1	$f(1) = 3(1) - 6 = -3$	-3
2	$f(2) = 3(2) - 6 = 0$	0
3	$f(3) = 3(3) - 6 = 3$	3
4	$f(4) = 3(4) - 6 = 6$	6

   This time, darken the endpoint at $(1, -3)$ because 1 is part of the domain for the second piece of the function.

SOLUTION   **The graph in Step 4 represents the piecewise function.**

Look back at Example 1. Notice that when finding the value of $f(-1)$, you used a different equation than when you found the value of $f(2)$. It is important to keep the domain in mind when working with piecewise functions.

Example 2 shows how an absolute value function can be represented as a piecewise function. Represent it as two **linear equations** across different domains.

To write these equations, you can use the **slope-intercept form** of a line:

   $y = mx + b$, where m represents the **slope** and b represents the **y-intercept**.

Below is how to find the slope of a line with points (x_1, y_1) and (x_2, y_2).

   $\text{slope} = m = \dfrac{\text{change in } y}{\text{change in } x} = \dfrac{y_2 - y_1}{x_2 - x_1}$

EXAMPLE 2

Write $f(x) = |x|$ as a piecewise function.

STRATEGY   **Graph the absolute value function. Then represent the function as a piecewise function.**

STEP 1   Make a table of values for the absolute value function and graph it.

   When choosing input numbers, include negative numbers, zero, and positive numbers.

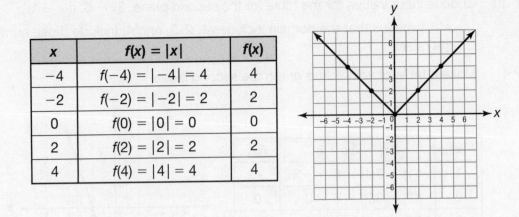

x	$f(x) = \lvert x \rvert$	$f(x)$
-4	$f(-4) = \lvert -4 \rvert = 4$	4
-2	$f(-2) = \lvert -2 \rvert = 2$	2
0	$f(0) = \lvert 0 \rvert = 0$	0
2	$f(2) = \lvert 2 \rvert = 2$	2
4	$f(4) = \lvert 4 \rvert = 4$	4

STEP 2   Which pieces of the function could be defined with linear equations?

The y-axis divides the graph into two different pieces, which could be defined as linear functions.

STEP 3   Write an equation for the first piece.

The first piece has input values less than 0. So the domain is $x < 0$.

Use the points $(-2, 2)$ and $(0, 0)$ to find the slope, m.

$$m = \frac{y_2 - y_1}{x_2 - x_1} = \frac{0 - 2}{0 - (-2)} = \frac{-2}{2} = -1$$

The y-intercept is at $(0, 0)$. So, $b = 0$.

The equation is: $f(x) = mx + b = -x + 0 = -x$.

So, the first piece is: $f(x) = -x$, if $x < 0$.

STEP 4   Write an equation for the second piece.

The second piece has input values greater than or equal to 0. So, the domain is $x \geq 0$.

Use the points $(0, 0)$, and $(2, 2)$ to find the slope.

$$m = \frac{y_2 - y_1}{x_2 - x_1} = \frac{2 - 0}{2 - 0} = \frac{2}{2} = 1$$

The y-intercept is at $(0, 0)$. So, $b = 0$.

The equation for the second piece is: $f(x) = mx + b = 1x + 0 = +x$.

So, the piecewise function is: $f(x) = \begin{cases} -x, \text{ if } x < 0 \\ +x, \text{ if } x \geq 0 \end{cases}$.

SOLUTION   **The piecewise function is written in Step 4.**

A function whose graph looks like steps on a staircase is called a **step function**. One type of step function is called a **ceiling function**. This function can be represented as $f(x) = \lceil x \rceil$, where $f(x)$ is equal to the least integer greater than or equal to the input value. Another type of step function is the **greatest integer function**. This function can be represented as $f(x) = [x]$, $f(x) = \lfloor x \rfloor$, or $f(x) = [\![x]\!]$, where $f(x)$ is equal to the greatest integer less than or equal to the input value. Greatest integer functions are also called **floor functions**.

EXAMPLE 3

Skyler is participating in a charity walk-a-thon. A sponsor will donate 0 dollars if Skyler walks less than a kilometer in total. The sponsor will give $1 to the charity for each kilometer or part of a kilometer (greater than 1 km) that Skyler walks. (So, if she walks $\frac{1}{2}$ km, the sponsor gives $0. If she walks 1 km, the sponsor gives $1.)

The total number of dollars the sponsor donates is defined by the floor function $f(x) = [x]$, $x \geq 0$. How many dollars will the sponsor give if Skyler walks 3 kilometers? 3.8 kilometers? 4.5 kilometers? Make a table and graph to show your answers are correct.

STRATEGY   **Use algebra to find the value of $f(3)$, $f(3.8)$, and $f(4.5)$. Then make a graph.**

STEP 1   Find $f(3)$, $f(3.8)$, and $f(4.5)$.

$f(3) = [3] =$ (the greatest integer ≤ 3) $= 3$

$f(3.8) = [3.8] =$ (the greatest integer ≤ 3.8) $= 3$

$f(4.5) = [4.5] =$ (the greatest integer ≤ 4.5) $= 4$

So, the sponsor gives $3 if Skyler walks a total of 3 or 3.8 km, and $4 if she walks a total of 4.5 km.

STEP 2   Make a table and a graph to represent the function.

Kilometers x	Dollars f(x)
$0 \leq x < 1$	0
$1 \leq x < 2$	1
$2 \leq x < 3$	2
$3 \leq x < 4$	3
$4 \leq x < 5$	4

On the graph, a horizontal line segment is drawn from (0, 0) up to (0, 1), from (1, 1) up to (1, 2), and so on to show the floor function.

The closed endpoints show points that are part of the graph. The open endpoints show points that are not part of the graph.

STEP 3   Do the table and graph show that your answers are correct?

The table and graph both show that when $x = 3$ and when $x = 3.8$, the $f(x)$ value is 3, and when $x = 4.5$, the $f(x)$ value is 4.

SOLUTION   **The sponsor gives $3 if Skyler walks 3 or 3.8 kilometers, and $4 if she walks 4.5 kilometers.**

COACHED EXAMPLE

Evaluate the greatest integer function below for $x = -3$ and $x = \frac{5}{4}$.

$f(x) = [x] + 3$

THINKING IT THROUGH

Use what you know about the greatest integer function.

$f(x) = [x] = $ (the greatest integer $\leq x$)

Find the value of $[-3]$.

$[-3] = $ (the greatest integer $[\leq -3] = $ _____)

Substitute that value into the new function.

$f(-3) = [-3] + 3 = $ _____ $+ 3 = $ _____

Find the value of $x = \frac{5}{4}$.

$\left[\frac{5}{4}\right] = $ (the greatest integer $\left[\leq \frac{5}{4}\right] = $ _____)

Substitute that value into the new function.

$f\left(\frac{5}{4}\right) = \left[\frac{5}{4}\right] + 3 = $ _____ $+ 3 = $ _____

When $x = -3$, the output value is _____ . When $x = \frac{5}{4}$, the output value is _____ .

Lesson Practice

Choose the correct answer.

1. Below is the graph of $f(x) = -|x|$.

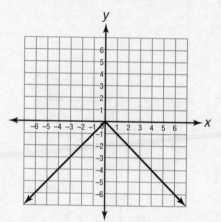

Which shows how this function could be represented as a piecewise function?

A. $f(x) = \begin{cases} -x, \text{ if } x < 0 \\ +x, \text{ if } x \geq 0 \end{cases}$

B. $f(x) = \begin{cases} +x, \text{ if } x < 0 \\ -x, \text{ if } x \geq 0 \end{cases}$

C. $f(x) = \begin{cases} -x, \text{ if } x < 1 \\ +x, \text{ if } x \geq 1 \end{cases}$

D. $f(x) = \begin{cases} +x, \text{ if } x < 1 \\ +x, \text{ if } x \geq 1 \end{cases}$

Use this function and graph for questions 2 and 3.

Below is the graph of the least integer function, $f(x) = \lceil x \rceil$.

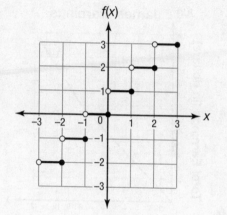

2. What is the value of $f\left(2\frac{1}{4}\right)$?

A. 3

B. $2\frac{1}{2}$

C. 2

D. -2

3. What is the value of $f\left(-\frac{1}{2}\right)$?

A. $\frac{1}{2}$

B. 0

C. $-\frac{1}{2}$

D. -1

Use this information for questions 4 and 5.

James earns an hourly wage for the first 8 hours he works in a day and overtime pay for any hours he works over 8 hours. The graph below represents how much money he could earn in a single day.

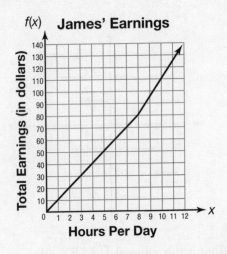

4. How much does James earn if he works 9 hours today?

   A. 80 dollars

   B. 90 dollars

   C. 95 dollars

   D. 100 dollars

5. Which shows how his daily earnings could be represented as a piecewise function?

   A. $f(x) = \begin{cases} 10x, \text{ if } 0 \le x \le 8 \\ 15x - 40, \text{ if } x > 8 \end{cases}$

   B. $f(x) = \begin{cases} 10x, \text{ if } 0 \le x \le 8 \\ 15x, \text{ if } x > 8 \end{cases}$

   C. $f(x) = \begin{cases} 10x, \text{ if } 0 \le x \le 8 \\ 15x - 40, \text{ if } x > 8 \end{cases}$

   D. $f(x) = \begin{cases} 10x, \text{ if } 0 \le x \le 9 \\ 15x, \text{ if } x > 9 \end{cases}$

6. Which graph represents this piecewise function?

$$f(x) = \begin{cases} -\frac{1}{2}x + 1, \text{ if } x < -2 \\ -2x - 2, \text{ if } x \ge -2 \end{cases}$$

A.
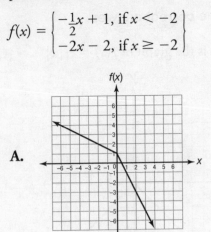

B.
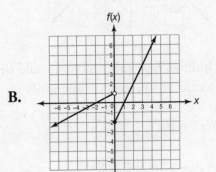

C.
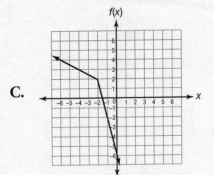

D.
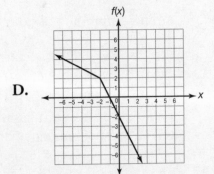

6 Characteristics of Piecewise Functions

MM2A1.b, MM2P3.a, MM2P3.d

The domain of a piecewise function is the set of all possible input values, or x-values.

The **range** of a piecewise function is the set of all possible output values, or $f(x)$-values.

The **maximum** (or absolute maximum) is the greatest value of y or $f(x)$ of a function. The **minimum** (or absolute minimum) is the least value of y or $f(x)$ of a function. The maximum and minimum of a graph are sometimes called the **extrema**.

The **vertex** of a quadratic or an absolute-value function is the minimum or maximum on the graph.

The **axis of symmetry** is the line that passes through the vertex and divides the graph into two congruent reflected halves.

EXAMPLE 1

Below is the graph of $f(x) = \begin{cases} -x + 2, & \text{if } x < 2 \\ x - 2, & \text{if } x \geq 2 \end{cases}$. Identify the domain and range of the function. Then identify the axis of symmetry and vertex of the graph.

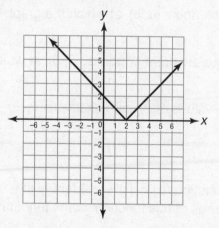

STRATEGY   Use the definitions of domain, range, vertex, and axis of symmetry.

STEP 1   Identify the domain.

The domain is the set of all x-values. The domain for this function includes all real numbers.

We could also say that the domain is $\{-\infty < x < \infty\}$.
(The symbol ∞ means "infinity.")

STEP 2   Identify the range.

The range is the set of all $f(x)$-values.

The range only includes numbers on or above the x-axis. So, the range is all real numbers greater than or equal to 0.

We could also say that the range is $\{0 \le f(x) < \infty\}$.

STEP 3   Label the vertex and axis of symmetry on the graph.

The graph has a minimum at (2, 0), so that is the vertex of the graph.

The axis of symmetry, $x = 2$, passes through the vertex and divides the function into two congruent halves.

SOLUTION   **The domain is the set of all real numbers. The range is the set of all real numbers greater than or equal to 0. The vertex is at (2, 0), and the axis of symmetry is the line $x = 2$.**

A **continuous function** is one whose graph can be drawn without lifting your pencil from the paper. If you must lift your pencil in order to draw the graph of a function, it is a **discontinuous function**. Any point at which you must lift your pencil is called a **point of discontinuity**.

The y-intercept of a function is the point, (0, b), at which the graph of the function crosses the y-axis.

The **x-intercepts** of a function are the point or points, (a, 0), at which the graph of the function crosses the x-axis.

The **zeros of a function** are any values of x that make $f(x) = 0$.

EXAMPLE 2

Below is the graph of the step function $f(x) = [x] - 1$. Identify the y-intercepts, x-intercepts, and zeros of this function. Is the function continuous or discontinuous?

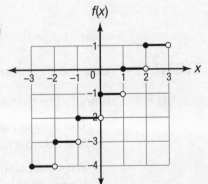

STRATEGY   **Use the definitions of intercepts, zeros, continuous functions, and discontinuous functions.**

STEP 1   Label the intercepts on the graph.

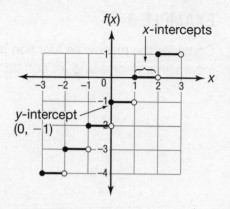

The graph crosses the y-axis at (0, −1), so that is the y-intercept.

The graph touches the x-axis at (1, 0) and continues to touch the axis along that line segment until it ends right before (2, 0).

So, the x-intercepts are on the interval {1 ≤ x < 2}. The notation means that x could be any number from 1 to 2, not including 2.

STEP 2   Identify the zeros of the function.

The zeros are the values of x that make f(x) = 0 true.

Looking at the x-intercepts, you can see that f(x) = 0 when x is greater than or equal to 1 and less than 2. Use the equation to test several x-values in that range. Remember, [x] = (the greatest integer ≤ x).

Test x = 1.

$f(x) = [x] − 1 = [1] − 1 = 1 − 1 = 0.$

Both of those values make f(x) = 0.

Test x = 1.99.

$f(x) = [x] − 1 = [1.99] − 1 = 1 − 1 = 0.$

STEP 3   Is the function continuous or discontinuous?

The graph "jumps" one unit vertically at each integer value.

So, the function is discontinuous. It has many points of discontinuity.

SOLUTION   **The graph has x-intercepts on the interval {1 ≤ x < 2} and a y-intercept at (0, −1). The zeros of the function are all real numbers greater than or equal to 1 and less than 2. The function is discontinuous.**

An **interval of increase** is a part of a function in which both the input values and output values are increasing.

An **interval of decrease** is a part of a function in which as input values increase, output values decrease.

A **constant interval** is a part of a function in which as input values increase, output values stay the same.

You can write an interval of increase, an interval of decrease, or a constant interval using interval notation.

Use parentheses when a value is not included in the interval and brackets when a value is included. For example, the notation (0,5] indicates that the interval includes all values greater than 0 and less than or equal to 5.

EXAMPLE 3

Consider the piecewise function graphed below. Identify any intervals on which the function is increasing, decreasing, or constant. Then identify its maximum and minimum values.

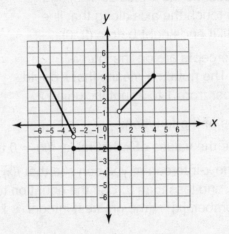

STRATEGY **Label the parts of the graph that are increasing or decreasing. Then label the maximum and minimum.**

STEP 1 Label the parts of the graph.

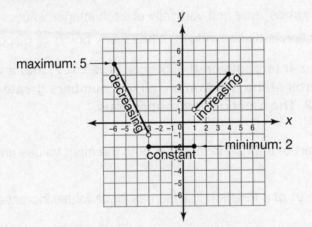

STEP 2 Use the graph to describe the intervals.

The graph falls and the $f(x)$-values decrease from $x = -6$ to just before $x = -3$. So, the graph is decreasing on the interval $[-6, -3)$ or $\{-6 \leq x < -3\}$.

The graph shows a horizontal line segment from $x = -3$ to $x = 1$. So, the graph is constant on the interval $[-3, 1]$ or $\{-3 \leq x \leq 1\}$.

The graph rises and the $f(x)$-values increase after $x = 1$ up to (and including) $x = 4$. So, the graph is increasing on the interval $(1, 4]$ or $\{1 < x \leq 4\}$.

STEP 3   Use the graph to describe the maximum and minimum.

The greatest *f*(*x*)-value shown on the graph is 5, so that is the maximum.

The least *f*(*x*)-value shown on the graph is −2, so that is the minimum.

SOLUTION   **The graph is increasing on the interval {−6 ≤ x < −3}, is constant on the interval {−3 ≤ x ≤ 1}, and is increasing on the interval {1 < x ≤ 4}. The maximum is 5. The minimum is −2.**

You should be able to interpret the rate of change shown by a piecewise function. The most basic example of a rate of change is the slope of a linear function. It is helpful to remember that a line with a positive slope rises from left to right. A line with a negative slope falls from left to right. Finally, a horizontal line has a slope of zero.

The slope of a linear function is constant. In a piecewise function, the rate of change often varies from piece to piece.

COACHED EXAMPLE

The graph below shows how the value of a mutual fund changed each business day for 10 days. Based on the graph, between which two days did the fund's price have a negative rate of change? Between which two days did the fund's price stay the same?

THINKING IT THROUGH

A line or line segment with a _____ slope falls from left to right.

The line segment on the graph that falls from left to right shows the change from Day _____ to Day _____.

A horizontal line or line segment has a slope of _____ and shows that output values are not changing.

The line segment on the graph that is horizontal shows the change from Day _____ to Day _____.

The rate of change in the fund's daily price was negative from Day _____ to Day _____ and the price stayed the same from Day _____ to Day _____.

Lesson Practice

Choose the correct answer.

Use this graph for questions 1 and 2.

Below is the graph of this piecewise function:

$$f(x) = \begin{cases} 4x + 2, \text{ if } -2 \le x < 1 \\ -x + 5, \text{ if } 1 \le x \le 6 \end{cases}.$$

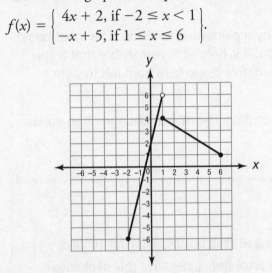

1. Which best describes the domain of this function?

    A. the set of all integers from -2 to 6

    B. the set of all real numbers greater than or equal to -2 and less than or equal to 6

    C. the set of all real numbers greater than or equal to -6 and less than or equal to 6

    D. the set of all real numbers greater than or equal to -2 and less than 6

2. Which is true of the function?

    A. The function has a point of discontinuity at (0, 6).

    B. The function is decreasing on the interval $\{-2 \le x < 1\}$.

    C. The function is increasing on the interval $\{-2 \le x < 1\}$.

    D. The function is constant on the interval $\{1 \le x \le 6\}$.

Use this information for questions 3 and 4.

The graph below shows how the cost of admission to an aquarium varies depending on a person's age.

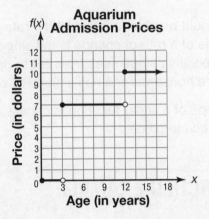

3. Which describes the range of the graph?

    A. {0, 7, 10}

    B. the set of all integers from 0 to 10

    C. the set of all real numbers greater than 0

    D. the set of all real numbers from 0 to 10

4. Which is true of the x-intercepts of the graph?

    A. The only x-intercept is at (0, 0).

    B. The x-intercepts are on the interval $\{0 \le x < 1\}$.

    C. The x-intercepts are on the interval $\{0 \le x < 3\}$.

    D. The x-intercepts are on the interval $\{0 \le x \le 3\}$.

Use this function for questions 5 and 6.

Below is the graph of this piecewise function:

$$f(x) = \begin{Bmatrix} -x - 6, \text{ if } x < -2 \\ x - 2, \text{ if } x \geq -1 \end{Bmatrix}.$$

5. Which names the axis of symmetry for this graph?

   A. $x = -2$

   B. $y = -4$

   C. the x-axis

   D. the y-axis

6. Which is **not** true of the function?

   A. The point at $(0, -2)$ is a y-intercept.

   B. The point at $(-2, -4)$ is a vertex.

   C. The minimum is -4.

   D. The zeros are -6 and -2.

7. Below is the graph of $y = \lfloor x \rfloor - 2$.

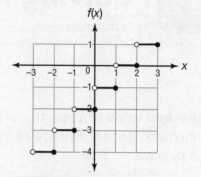

Which is **not** true of the function?

   A. It is discontinuous because it "jumps" one unit vertically at each integer value.

   B. The domain is $\{-\infty < x < \infty\}$.

   C. It is constant on the interval $\{-2 < x \leq -1\}$.

   D. It is increasing on the interval $\{-3 < x \leq -2\}$.

8. The graph below shows the distance that the Alston family drove over the course of six hours.

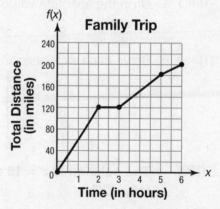

During which time period was the rate of change 0 miles per hour?

   A. during the first two hours

   B. between hours 2 and 3

   C. between hours 3 and 5

   D. between hours 5 and 6

7 Solving Absolute Value Equations

MM2A1.c, MM2P1.c

The **absolute value** of a quantity, written using the symbols | |, is its distance from zero on a number line. Since a distance cannot be negative, the absolute value of any real number is always positive.

For example, both absolute values below are equal to 5.

$$x = |5| = 5 \qquad x = |-5| = 5$$

Because of this, if we are given $|x| = 5$, then there are two possible x-values. The variable x may be equal to either 5 *or* −5.

To solve an absolute value equation, set the expression inside the absolute value symbols equal to its positive value and its negative value. Then solve for both values.

EXAMPLE 1

Solve $\left|\frac{1}{2}x + 1\right| = 9$.

STRATEGY Drop the absolute value symbols. Solve for the expression equal to 9 and for the expression equal to −9.

> **STEP 1** Drop the absolute value symbols. Set the expression inside equal to 9 and −9.
>
> $$\frac{1}{2}x + 1 = 9 \qquad or \qquad \frac{1}{2}x + 1 = -9$$
>
> **STEP 2** Solve each expression.
>
> | | |
> |---|---|
> | $\frac{1}{2}x + 1 = 9$ | $\frac{1}{2}x + 1 = -9$ |
> | $\frac{1}{2}x = 8$ | $\frac{1}{2}x = -10$ |
> | $x = 16$ | $x = -20$ |

SOLUTION The solution is $x = 16$ or $x = -20$. This solution set can also be written as {16, −20}.

You can also solve an absolute value equation graphically. Take the expression or value on each side of the equation and set it equal to y. Then graph both functions and find the points at which they intersect. The x-values of those points are the solutions to the equation.

EXAMPLE 2

Solve $|2x + 2| = 4$.

STRATEGY **Set each side of the equation equal to y. Graph the functions and find the x-values of their points of intersection.**

STEP 1   Set each side of the equation equal to y.

$y = |2x + 2|$ and $y = 4$.

STEP 2   Graph both functions on the same coordinate grid and label the points of intersection.

Make a table for $y = |2x + 2|$. There is no need to make a table for $y = 4$, because it is a horizontal line.

x	$y = |2x + 2|$	$f(x)$
-3	$y = |2(-3) + 2| = 4$	4
-2	$y = |2(-2) + 2| = 2$	2
-1	$y = |2(-1) + 2| = 0$	0
0	$y = |2(0) + 2| = 2$	2
1	$y = |2(1) + 2| = 4$	4

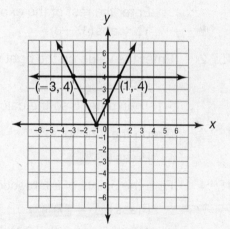

The x-values for the points of intersection are -3 and 1. So, those are the solutions.

SOLUTION $x = -3$ or $x = 1$

You can also use technology, such as a graphing calculator, to solve absolute value equations. Instead of drawing a graph as you did in Example 2, use your calculator to do the graphing and find the points of intersection. **Note:** Depending on which calculator model you have, you may need to press slightly different keys on your calculator to perform the functions in this or other examples in the book.

EXAMPLE 3

Solve $|4x - 3| = 5$.

STRATEGY   **Use a graphing calculator.**

STEP 1   Enter the expression on the left side of the equation as Y_1.

Press `Y=`.

Press `MATH` ▶ **NUM**. Press **1** to select **1: abs(**

Now, the calculator reads: $Y_1 = $ abs(

Enter the rest of the expression on the left side so the screen reads:
$Y_1 = $ abs$(4X-3)$

STEP 2   Enter the value on the right side of the equation as Y_2.

Press `ENTER`.

Then enter 5 so the calculator reads: $Y_2 = 5$.

STEP 3   Graph the functions.

Press `GRAPH`.

STEP 4   Find the points of intersection.

Press `2nd` `TRACE`.

This brings up the **CALCULATE** menu. Press **5** to select **5:intersect**.

Use the arrow keys to move the cursor close to one of the points of intersection.

Press `ENTER`. Then press `ENTER` two more times.

The calculator shows that the x-value of one of the points of intersection is -0.5.

Repeat this process to find the x-value of the second point of intersection.

Intersection
X=−.5   Y=5

Intersection
X=2   Y=5

SOLUTION $x = -0.5$ or $x = 2$

COACHED EXAMPLE

Solve $|-5x| = 10$.

THINKING IT THROUGH

Drop the absolute value symbols. Set the expression $-5x$ equal to 10 and -10. Solve each.

$-5x =$ _____   *or* $-5x =$ _____

_____   _____

_____   _____

The solution is $x =$ _____ or $x =$ _____.

Lesson Practice

Choose the correct answer.

1. What is the solution set for $|2x + 3| = 9$?

   A. $\{-9, 9\}$

   B. $\{-6, -3\}$

   C. $\{-6, 3\}$

   D. $\{-3, 6\}$

2. To solve $|2x - 2| = 6$, Navi graphed $y = |2x - 2|$ and $y = 6$, as shown below.

   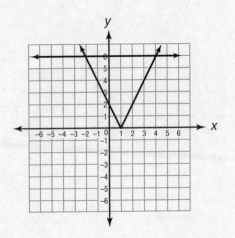

   What are the solutions for this equation?

   A. $x = -6$ or $x = 6$

   B. $x = -2$ or $x = 4$

   C. $x = -2$ or $x = 6$

   D. $x = 4$ or $x = 6$

3. What are the solutions for $-|2x| = -8$?

   A. $x = -4$ or $x = 4$

   B. $x = -4$ or $x = 8$

   C. $x = -8$ or $x = 4$

   D. $x = -8$ or $x = 8$

4. What is the solution set for $|6x + 2| = 3$?

   A. $\{-5, 1\}$

   B. $\{-1, 5\}$

   C. $\left\{-\frac{5}{6}, -\frac{1}{6}\right\}$

   D. $\left\{\frac{1}{6}, -\frac{5}{6}\right\}$

5. What are the solutions for $|3 - x| = 4$?

   A. $x = -1$ or $x = -7$

   B. $x = -1$ or $x = 7$

   C. $x = 1$ or $x = 4$

   D. $x = -7$ or $x = 1$

6. To solve $|x| = -2$, Ella graphed $y = |x|$ and $y = -2$ on her calculator.

   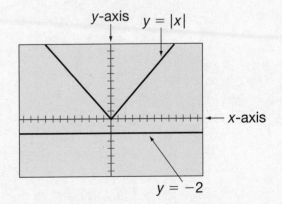

   What are the solutions for this absolute value equation?

   A. The solution is $x = 0$.

   B. The solution is $x = -2$.

   C. There are an infinite number of solutions.

   D. There are no solutions.

8 Solving Absolute Value Inequalities

MM2A1.c, MM2P1.c

You can use what you know about solving absolute value equations to help you solve absolute value inequalities. Begin solving the inequality as if you were solving an equation. Plot those values on a number line. Then decide which sections of the number line are included in the solution for the inequality.

EXAMPLE 1

What is the solution set for $|3x - 4| < 14$?

STRATEGY   **Drop the inequality sign and solve as if it were an equation. Plot the values of x on a number line. Test values on both sides of those points to determine whether they make the inequality true or not.**

STEP 1   Replace the less than ($<$) symbol with an equal ($=$) sign and solve.

$$3x - 4 = 14 \qquad \text{or} \qquad 3x - 4 = -14$$
$$3x = 18 \qquad\qquad\qquad 3x = -10$$
$$x = 6 \qquad\qquad\qquad\quad x = -\frac{10}{3}$$

STEP 2   Plot those points on a number line and choose test values.

The less than ($<$) symbol means that $-\frac{10}{3}$ and 6 are not possible values of x. So, draw open circles for those points.

This divides the number line into three sections. Identify one number in each section to test.

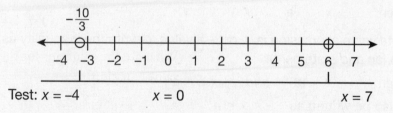

STEP 3   Test each of those numbers.

Test $x = -4$.

$$|3(-4) - 4| \overset{?}{\leq} 14$$
$$|-16| \overset{?}{\leq} 14$$

16 is *not* less than 14, so -4 is *not* a solution.

Test $x = 0$.

$$|3(0) - 4| \overset{?}{\leq} 14$$
$$|-4| \overset{?}{\leq} 14$$

4 *is* less than 14, so 0 *is* a solution.

Test $x = 7$.

$$|3(7) - 4| \overset{?}{\leq} 14$$
$$|17| \overset{?}{\leq} 14$$

17 is *not* less than 14, so 7 is *not* a solution.

STEP 4   Graph the solution.

Since $x = 0$ is a solution and $x = -4$ and $x = 7$ are not solutions, the solution set is all numbers between $-\frac{10}{3}$ and 6.

SOLUTION   The solution set is $-\frac{10}{3} < x < 6$.

Another way to determine the solution set of an absolute-value inequality is to rewrite it as a compound inequality. Follow these rules:

> If the absolute value expression is $>$ or $\geq$ a value, rewrite the inequality as a **disjunction** (an *or* statement).
>
> If $|x| > a$, then $\qquad x < -a \qquad$ or $\qquad x > a$
>
> If the absolute value expression is $<$ or $\leq$ a value, rewrite the inequality as a **conjunction** (an *and* statement).
>
> If $|x| < a$, then $\qquad x < a \qquad$ and $\qquad x > -a$
>
> This could also be written as $-a < x < a$.

EXAMPLE 2

What is the solution set for $|-4x + 3| \geq 23$?

STRATEGY **Use the rules to write the inequality as a compound inequality. Then solve.**

STEP 1   Is the inequality a disjunction or a conjunction?

The absolute value expression is greater than or equal to ($\geq$) 23.

Rewrite the inequality as a disjunction, using the word *or*.

STEP 2   Write the two inequalities. For the second inequality, reverse the inequality symbol and make 23 negative.

$$-4x + 3 \geq 23 \qquad or \qquad -4x + 3 \leq -23$$

STEP 3   Solve. Remember to reverse the inequality sign if you multiply or divide both sides by a negative number.

$$
\begin{array}{c|c}
-4x + 3 \geq 23 & -4x + 3 \leq -23 \\
-4x \geq 20 & -4x \leq -26 \\
x \leq -5 & x \geq \frac{13}{2} \text{ or } x \geq 6.5
\end{array}
$$

STEP 4   Graph the solution.

To check if the solution to an inequality is correct, choose *x*-values that are and are not included on the graph and test them to see if they make the original inequality true.

SOLUTION $x \leq -5$ or $x \geq 6.5$

You can also use a graphing calculator to solve absolute value inequalities. This method is similar to how you used a graphing calculator to solve absolute value equations in Lesson 7, but with a few additional steps. If you need to review which calculator keys to press to perform some of the functions mentioned below, look back at Example 3 in Lesson 7 on page 52.

EXAMPLE 3

What is the solution set for $|1 - x| \leq 2$?

STRATEGY   **Use a graphing calculator.**

STEP 1   Enter the expression on the left side of the equation as Y_1, and the expression on the right side of the equation as Y_2.

Enter: $Y_1 = \text{abs}(1 - X)$

Enter: $Y_2 = 2$

STEP 2   Now, enter the inequality as Y_3.

Move to the $Y_3 =$ prompt.

Press VARS ▶ **Y-VARS**.

Press **1** to select **1:Function...** and then **1** to select **1:Y₁**.

Press 2nd MATH .

This brings up the **TEST** Menu, where you will find the inequality symbols.

Press **6** to select **6:≤**.

Then press VARS ▶ **Y-VARS** again.

Press **1** to select **1:Function...** and then **2** to select **2:Y₂**.

The calculator now reads: $Y_3 = Y_1 \leq Y_2$

STEP 3   Press GRAPH to graph the equations and the inequality.

The part of the graph where $Y_3 = 1$ shows the solution set for the inequality.

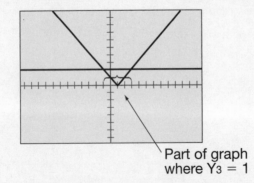

Part of graph
where Y3 = 1

    Duplicating any part of this book is prohibited by law.

STEP 4   Look at the table.

Press [2nd] [GRAPH].

Use the 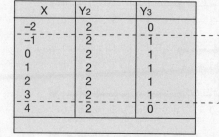 to look at the column for Y_3 in the table. For any x-value that is a solution, a 1 will be in that column. For any x-value that is *not* part of the solution set, a 0 is in that column.

X	Y₂	Y₃
−2	2	0
−1	2	1
0	2	1
1	2	1
2	2	1
3	2	1
4	2	0

The solution set is $-1 \leq x \leq 3$.

STEP 5   Graph the solution on a number line.

-1 and 3 are possible values of x, so draw closed endpoints.

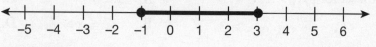

SOLUTION $-1 \leq x \leq 3$

COACHED EXAMPLE

What is the solution set for $2|x - 5| < 8$?

THINKING IT THROUGH

Divide both sides of the inequality by 2 to get the absolute value expression by itself.

$2|x - 5| < 8 =$ _____

Should you rewrite the inequality as a disjunction or a conjunction?

The absolute value expression is less than ($<$) a certain number.

So, rewrite the inequality as a _____.

Write the two inequalities. For the second inequality, reverse the inequality symbol and make the value on the right side negative.

_____   *and*   _____

Solve each.

_____   *and*   _____

Graph the solution.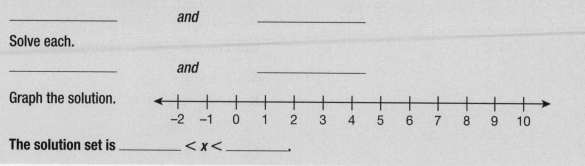

The solution set is _____ $< x <$ _____.

Lesson Practice

Choose the correct answer.

1. Which best represents the graph of $|x + 3| \geq 2$?

   A. ![number line graph]

   B. ![number line graph]

   C. ![number line graph]

   D. ![number line graph]

2. What is the solution set for $|5x| > 15$?

   A. $x > 3$
   B. $-3 < x < 3$
   C. $x < -3$ or $x > 3$
   D. $x < -3$

3. What is the solution set for $|3x| + 2 < 14$?

   A. $x > 4$
   B. $-4 < x < 4$
   C. $x < -4$ or $x > 4$
   D. $x < -4$

4. What is the solution set for $|2x - 7| \leq 3$?

   A. $x \leq -5$ or $x \geq 2$
   B. $x \leq 2$ or $x \geq 5$
   C. $-5 \leq x \leq 2$
   D. $2 \leq x \leq 5$

5. What is the solution set for $|4x - 3| \geq 6$?

   A. $x \leq -\frac{3}{4}$ or $x \geq \frac{9}{4}$
   B. $-\frac{3}{4} \leq x \leq \frac{9}{4}$
   C. $x \leq -\frac{9}{4}$ or $x \geq \frac{3}{2}$
   D. $-\frac{9}{4} \leq x \leq \frac{3}{4}$

6. Which best represents the graph of $3|x - 4| < 9$?

   A. ![number line graph]

   B. ![number line graph]

   C. ![number line graph]

   D. ![number line graph]

7. What is the solution set for $|-3x| \geq 21$?

   A. $x \geq 7$
   B. $-7 \leq x \leq 7$
   C. $x \leq -7$ or $x \geq 7$
   D. $x \leq -7$

8. Max is solving $|2 - x| \geq 2$. He correctly entered the following into his graphing calculator:

   $$Y_1 = \text{abs}(2 - x)$$
   $$Y_2 = 2$$
   $$Y_3 = Y_1 \geq Y_2$$

   He then looked at this table on his calculator.

   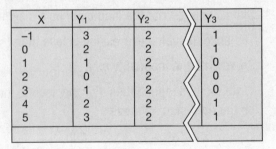

X	Y1	Y2	Y3
-1	3	2	1
0	2	2	1
1	1	2	0
2	0	2	0
3	1	2	0
4	2	2	1
5	3	2	1

   Based on these results, what is the solution?

   A. $x \leq 0$ or $x \geq 4$
   B. $x \leq -4$ or $x \geq 0$
   C. $0 \geq x \geq 4$
   D. $-4 \geq x \geq 0$

9 Basic Exponential Functions

MM2A2.e, MM2P1.b, MM2P4.c, MM2P5.c

An **exponential function** is written in the form $f(x) = a^x$, where the base a is a constant that is greater than 0 and the exponent x is any real number. Exponential functions can be used to model real-world situations.

EXAMPLE 1

A scientist puts a single microorganism in a culture broth. Every hour, the number of microorganisms in the broth doubles. Graph this function to show the number of microorganisms in the broth after x hours: $f(x) = 2^x$, where $x \geq 0$.

About how many microorganisms are in the broth after 3.5 hours?

STRATEGY   **Make a table of values and graph the function. Estimate the number of microorganisms after 3.5 hours.**

STEP 1   Make a table of values. Plot the points and connect them.

x	$f(x) = 2^x$	$f(x)$
0	$f(0) = (2^0) = 1$	1
1	$f(1) = (2^1) = 2$	2
2	$f(2) = (2^2) = 4$	4
3	$f(3) = (2^3) = 8$	8
4	$f(4) = (2^4) = 16$	16

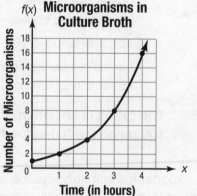

Note: You cannot draw a straight line through the points. You must draw a curve.

STEP 2   How many microorganisms are there after 3.5 hours?

Find $x = 3.5$ on the graph. At that point, the output value is about 11. You could also use the equation and a calculator to determine this: $f(x) = 2^x = 2^{3.5} \approx 11.3$.

Both methods show that there will be about 11 microorganisms in the broth.

SOLUTION   **The graph is shown in Step 2. After 3.5 hours, there will be about 11 microorganisms in the broth.**

EXAMPLE 2

A scientist puts 100 microorganisms in a culture broth. Every hour, the number of microorganisms in the broth doubles. Graph this function to show the number of microorganisms in the broth after x hours: $g(x) = 100(2^x)$, where $x \geq 0$.

How does this function compare with the function in Example 1?

STRATEGY   **Make a table of values and graph the function. Compare the functions.**

STEP 1   Make a table of values. Plot the points and connect them.

x	$g(x) = 100(2^x)$	$g(x)$
0	$g(0) = 100(2^0) = 100$	100
1	$g(1) = 100(2^1) = 200$	200
2	$g(2) = 100(2^2) = 400$	400
3	$g(3) = 100(2^3) = 800$	800
4	$g(4) = 100(2^4) = 1,600$	1,600

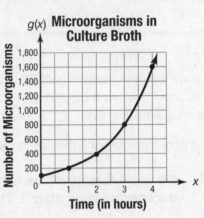

STEP 2   Compare this function to the one in Example 1.

Look at the equations. The only difference between the equations for $f(x)$ and $g(x)$ is that the equation for $g(x)$ is multiplied by 100.

Each $g(x)$-value is 100 times the $f(x)$-value for the same input value.

This makes sense. In Example 1, the broth started with 1 microorganism. In Example 2, the broth started with 100 microorganisms.

SOLUTION   **The graph is shown in Step 1. Each $g(x)$-value for the function in Example 2 is 100 times the $f(x)$-value for the same input value in Example 1.**

The basic exponential function was the same for both Examples 1 and 2. Both included 2^x and both functions involved the growth of a population of microorganisms. The difference was that in Example 2, there were 100 microorganisms at the start instead of one. So, 100 was multiplied by 2^x to model the second function.

The two examples above lead us to a formula. To model exponential growth or decay with a constant percent increase or decrease, we can use this formula: $f(t) = a(1 \pm r)^t$, where a is the initial population, r is the rate of increase or decrease, and t is the number of time periods.

Example 3 applies this formula to an exponential decay function.

EXAMPLE 3

The value of a computer bought new for $1,000 decreases by 20% each year. Write an exponential function and graph it. How does the graph for an exponential decay function differ from the graph for an exponential growth function?

STRATEGY   **Use the formula to write the function and graph it.**

    STEP 1   Use the formula.

           The value *decreases*, so write an exponential decay function.

           The initial amount, *a*, is $1,000.

           The rate of the decrease is 20% or 0.2.

           Use *x* to represent the number of time periods.

           $f(x) = 1000(1 - 0.2)^x = 1000(0.8)^x$

    STEP 2   Make a table of values. Graph the function.

           Use a graphing calculator to help you create the table.

           You may also choose to graph the function on your calculator.

x	$f(x) = 1000(0.8^x)$	$f(x)$
0	$f(0) = 1000(0.8^0) = 1000$	1,000
1	$f(1) = 1000(0.8^1) = 800$	800
2	$f(2) = 1000(0.8^2) = 640$	640
3	$f(3) = 1000(0.8^3) = 512$	512
4	$f(4) = 1000(0.8^4) = 409.6$	409.6

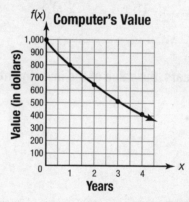

Computer's Value

    STEP 3   How does this graph differ from the graphs of exponential growth functions?

           The graph of an exponential decay function, like the graph in Step 3, shows that as input values increase, output values decrease. So, it curves downward.

           The graph of an exponential growth function, like the graph in Example 1, shows that as input values increase, output values also increase. So, it curves upward.

SOLUTION   **The function is $f(x) = 1000(0.8)^x$. Its graph is shown in Step 2. The graph of an exponential decay function shows that as input values increase, output values decrease.**

Another common example of exponential growth in the real world is **compound interest**.

COACHED EXAMPLE

Jeremy invests $200 at a rate of 5% interest compounded yearly. This formula can be used to calculate the amount, A, that the investment will be worth after t years: $A = P(1 + r)^t$, where P is the principal (amount invested) and r is the rate. How much will Jeremy's investment be worth after 12 years? Assume that he makes no deposits or withdrawals.

THINKING IT THROUGH

Use the formula to find the value of the investment after 5 years.

Substitute _____ for the principal, P.

The rate, r, is 5%, so convert it to a decimal before substituting it for r: 5% = _____.

Substitute 12 for the time, t.

$A = P(1 + r)^t$

$A =$ _____ $\cdot (1 +$ _____ $)^{12}$

$A \approx$ _____

After 12 years, the value of the investment will be about $ _____.

Lesson Practice

Choose the correct answer.

1. A ball is dropped from a height of 512 centimeters. It rebounds to $\frac{1}{2}$ that height on the first bounce. On each subsequent bounce, it rebounds to $\frac{1}{2}$ its previous height. The function $f(x) = 512\left(\frac{1}{2}\right)^x$ represents the rebound height of the ball for bounce x. Which table best represents this situation?

A.

x	f(x)
0	512
1	256
2	128
3	64

B.

x	f(x)
0	64
1	128
2	256
3	512

C.

x	f(x)
0	1
1	0.5
2	0.25
3	0.125

D.

x	f(x)
0	1
1	256
2	65,536
3	16,777,216

Use this information for questions 2 and 3.

The formula for finding the amount of an investment with interest compounded yearly for t years is: $A = P(1 + r)^t$, where A is the amount invested or borrowed, P is the principal, and r is the rate.

2. Ariana invests $2,000 at a rate of 6% interest compounded yearly. Approximately how much will Ariana's investment be worth in 3 years?

   A. $432

   B. $2,382

   C. $8,192

   D. $686,000

3. Peter borrows $5,000 at a rate of 8% interest compounded yearly. He will pay it off in t years. Which equation best represents A, the total amount he must pay back, including interest?

   A. $A = 8(5000)^t$

   B. $A = 5000(1 + t)^8$

   C. $A = 5000(1.8)^t$

   D. $A = 5000(1.08)^t$

4. A scientist puts a single bacterium in a culture broth. Every day, the number of bacteria in the broth triples, as represented by the function $f(x) = 3^x$. Which graph best represents this function?

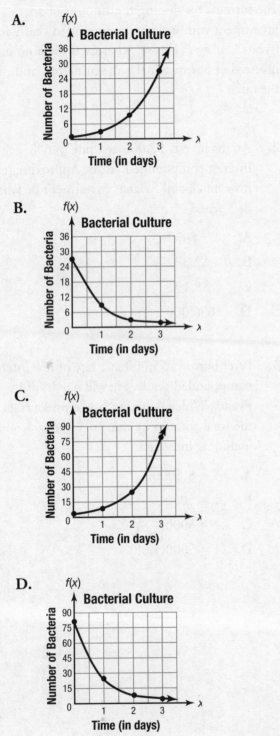

A.

B.

C.

D.

5. A new car is bought for $20,000. Its value decreases 15% each year, as represented by the function $f(x) = 20,000(0.85)^x$, where x is the age of the car in years. Which graph best represents this function?

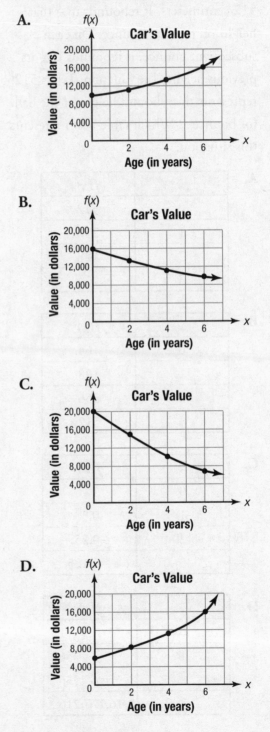

A.

B.

C.

D.

10 Characteristics of Exponential Functions

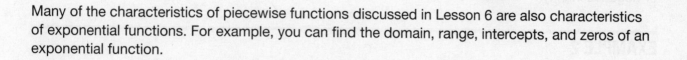

MM2A2.b, MM2P3.a, MM2P3.d

Many of the characteristics of piecewise functions discussed in Lesson 6 are also characteristics of exponential functions. For example, you can find the domain, range, intercepts, and zeros of an exponential function.

EXAMPLE 1

To the right is the graph of the function $f(x) = 4^x$. Identify the domain, range, y-intercept, x-intercept, and zeros of the function.

STRATEGY **Use the definitions of domain, range, intercepts, and zeros.**

STEP 1 Identify the domain and the range.

The domain is the set of all x-values.

For this function, the domain includes all real numbers. The domain is $\{-\infty < x < \infty\}$.

The range is the set of all $f(x)$-values.

The graph of the function comes close to, but never touches, the x-axis.

The range is all positive numbers greater than zero. The range is $\{0 < f(x) < \infty\}$.

STEP 2 Identify the intercepts.

The graph crosses the y-axis at (0, 1). So, that is the y-intercept.

The graph will never touch the x-axis. So, the function has no x-intercept.

STEP 3 Identify the zeros.

The zeros of a function are any values of x that make $f(x) = 0$.

The graph never touches the x-axis, which would be the point at which $f(x)$ would equal zero. So, this function has no zeros.

SOLUTION **The domain is the set of all real numbers. The range is all positive numbers greater than zero. The y-intercept is at (0, 1). The graph of the function has no x-intercepts and no zeros.**

A piecewise function can have intervals of increase and intervals of decrease, but an exponential function is either always increasing or always decreasing.

An **asymptote** is a line that a graphed function approaches but never crosses as it moves away from the origin.

End behavior describes what happens to $f(x)$-values as x-values approach either positive infinity or negative infinity.

EXAMPLE 2

Below is the graph of the function $f(x) = \left(\frac{1}{3}\right)^x$. Identify the function as either increasing or decreasing. Then identify the asymptote and describe the end behavior of the function.

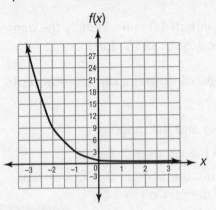

STRATEGY   **Determine if the function is increasing or decreasing. Then look at the ends.**

STEP 1   Is the function increasing or decreasing?

The graph curves downward from left to right.

As the x-values increase, the $f(x)$-values decrease. The function is decreasing.

STEP 2   Look at the left end of the function.

The arrow at the left end points upward, so the $f(x)$-values are approaching infinity.

This means that the function will increase without bound as x approaches negative infinity, or as $x \to -\infty$.

STEP 3   Look at the right end of the function.

As is moves away from the origin, the arrow at the right end gets closer and closer to, but does not touch or cross, the x-axis. The x-axis is the asymptote. The function asymptotically approaches 0 as x approaches infinity, or as $x \to \infty$.

SOLUTION   **The function is decreasing. Its asymptote is the x-axis. The function increases without bound as x approaches negative infinity, and asymptotically approaches 0 as x approaches positive infinity.**

You can also interpret the rate of change shown by the graph of an exponential function.

> If as *x*-values increase, *f(x)*-values also increase, the graph shows a positive rate of change.
>
> If as *x*-values increase, *f(x)*-values decrease, the graph shows a negative rate of change.

In a graphed line, the rate of change is constant. If a graph is a curve, it will have a variable rate of change. You can understand the rate of change for an exponential function by looking at the average rate of change for different points on a graph.

EXAMPLE 3

There are 10 cells in a solution. Every day, the number of cells in the solution doubles, as represented by the function $f(x) = 10(2^x)$ and the graph on the right. Briefly describe the rate of change for this function.

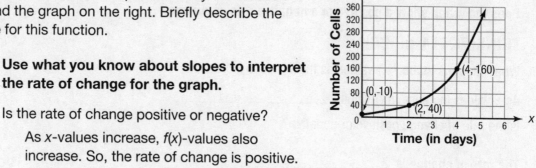

STRATEGY **Use what you know about slopes to interpret the rate of change for the graph.**

STEP 1   Is the rate of change positive or negative?

As *x*-values increase, *f(x)*-values also increase. So, the rate of change is positive.

This is an exponential growth function.

STEP 2   Find the average rate of change between different points on the graph.

Since the graph is not a straight line, the change in the number of cells, *f(x)*, depends on the values of *x* used.

The average rate of change for the function between (0, 10) and (2, 40) is:

$$\frac{y_2 - y_1}{x_2 - x_1} = \frac{40 - 10}{2 - 0} = \frac{30}{2} = 15 \text{ cells per day}$$

The average rate of change for the function between (2, 40) and (4, 160) is:

$$\frac{y_2 - y_1}{x_2 - x_1} = \frac{160 - 40}{4 - 2} = \frac{120}{2} = 60 \text{ cells per day}$$

STEP 3   Compare the average rate of change between the different points on the graph.

The average rate of change between (0, 10) and (2, 40) is 15 cells per day. The average rate of change between (2, 40) and (4, 160) is 60 cells per day.

The rate at which the number of cells is increasing in the solution is increasing over time. You can see this on the graph because the function gets steeper as the values of *x* increase.

SOLUTION **The function has a variable rate of change. The rate of change is always positive, but it becomes more rapid as time passes.**

COACHED EXAMPLE

Radium has a half-life of 1,599 years. The graph below shows what happens to 10 kilograms of radium over time.

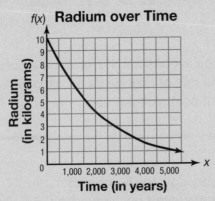

Radium over Time

Does the graph show a positive or a negative rate of change?

THINKING IT THROUGH

What happens to the f(x)-values as the x-values increase?

As x-values increase, f(x)-values _____.

Is the rate of change positive or negative?

The rate of change is _____.

Lesson Practice

Choose the correct answer.

Use the graph of $f(x) = 5^x$ for questions 1 and 2.

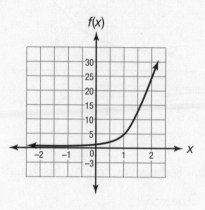

1. Which statement for this function is **not** true?

   A. The function is increasing.

   B. The domain is on the interval $\{-\infty < x < \infty\}$.

   C. The range is on the interval $\{0 < x < \infty\}$.

   D. The x-intercept is at $(-2, 0)$.

2. What is the asymptote for this function?

   A. the x-axis

   B. the y-axis

   C. $y = 1$

   D. $y = -1$

Use the graph of $f(x) = \left(\frac{1}{2}\right)^x - 4$ for questions 3 and 4.

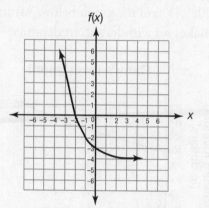

3. Which statement is true about the zeros of this function?

   A. The zero for this function is -3.

   B. The zero for this function is -2.

   C. This function has two zeros: -2 and -3.

   D. This function has no zeros.

4. Which best describes the range for this function?

   A. all real numbers greater than -4

   B. all real numbers less than -4

   C. the set of all integers

   D. the set of all real numbers

Use this information for questions 5 and 6.

Cami invests $500 at a rate of 10% compounded yearly. The amount of money in the account, A, over t years can be represented by the function $A = 500(1.1)^t$ and the graph below. Assume that Cami makes no withdrawals or deposits.

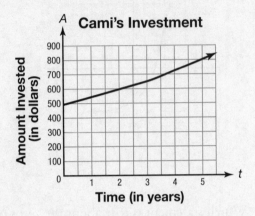

Use the graph of $f(x) = 2^x + 1$ for questions 7 and 8.

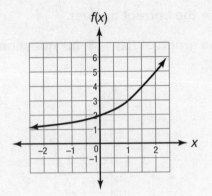

5. Which statement about Cami's investment is **not** true?

   A. The rate of change is positive.

   B. The rate of change is constant.

   C. The rate of change is variable.

   D. The average rate of change increases over time.

6. What is the y-intercept for this function?

   A. This function has no y-intercept.

   B. $(0, 0)$

   C. $(0, 500)$

   D. $(1, 550)$

7. What is the asymptote of this function?

   A. the x-axis

   B. the y-axis

   C. $y = -1$

   D. $y = 1$

8. Which statement is true about the end behavior of this function?

   A. The function is decreasing.

   B. The function asymptotically approaches 0 as $x \to \infty$.

   C. The function will increase without bound as $x \to \infty$.

   D. The function will increase without bound as $x \to -\infty$.

11 Solving Exponential Equations

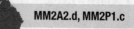

MM2A2.d, MM2P1.c

You can use the **one-to-one property** to solve simple exponential equations.

> **One-to-One Property**
>
> For $a > 0$ and $a \neq 1$, $a^x = a^y$ if and only if $x = y$.

EXAMPLE 1

Solve: $4^{x+1} = 4^7$

STRATEGY Use the one-to-one property.

STEP 1 Are the bases the same?

Yes, the base is 4 on both sides of the equation.

STEP 2 Use the one-to-one property to solve.

$4^{x+1} = 4^7$ if and only if $x + 1 = 7$.

Set the exponents equal to one another and solve for x:

$x + 1 = 7$

$x = 6$

SOLUTION $x = 6$

If the bases on either side of the equal sign of an exponential equation are not the same, try rewriting them to make them the same. Then use the one-to-one property to solve.

EXAMPLE 2

Solve: $5^{9+x} = 25^x$

STRATEGY   **Use the one-to-one property.**

STEP 1   Are the bases the same?

No, the base on the left is 5 and the base on the right is 25.

STEP 2   Rewrite each side with the same base.

25 is a power of 5, so rewrite the right side.

$5^{9+x} = 25^x$

$5^{9+x} = (5^2)^x$

$5^{9+x} = 5^{2x}$

STEP 3   Use the one-to-one property to solve.

$5^{9+x} = 5^{2x}$ if and only if $9 + x = 2x$.

Set the exponents equal to one another and solve for x:

$9 + x = 2x$

$9 = x$

SOLUTION   **$x = 9$**

Another way to solve exponential equations is to graph them. You can draw the graph yourself or use a graphing calculator.

EXAMPLE 3

Solve $2^{2x-2} = 16$ graphically.

STRATEGY   **Set each side of the equation equal to y. Graph the functions and find the x-values of their points of intersection.**

STEP 1   Set each side of the equation equal to y.

$y = 2^{2x-2}$ and $y = 16$.

STEP 2   Graph both functions on the same coordinate grid and label the points of intersection.

Make a table for $y = 2^{2x-2}$. There is no need to make a table for $y = 16$, since it is a horizontal line.

x	$f(x) = 2^{2x-2}$	$f(x)$
−1	$f(-1) = 2^{2(-1)-2} = \frac{1}{16}$	$\frac{1}{16}$
0	$f(0) = 2^{2(0)-2} = \frac{1}{4}$	$\frac{1}{4}$
1	$f(1) = 2^{2(1)-2} = 1$	1
2	$f(2) = 2^{2(2)-2} = 4$	4
3	$f(3) = 2^{2(3)-2} = 16$	16

The x-value for the point of intersection is 3, so 3 is the solution.

SOLUTION $x = 3$

You can also use technology, such as a graphing calculator, to solve exponential equations. Instead of drawing a graph, use your calculator to do the graphing and find the point of intersection. To review how to enter expressions, graph functions, or find points of intersection on a graphing calculator, look back at Lesson 7, Example 3, on page 52.

EXAMPLE 4

Solve $3^x = 9^{x-1}$ using technology.

STRATEGY   **Use a graphing calculator.**

STEP 1   Enter the expression on the left side of the equation as Y_1.
Enter: $Y_1 = 3^X$.

STEP 2   Enter the value on the right side of the equation as Y_2.
Enter: $Y_2 = 9^{X-1}$.

STEP 3   Graph the functions on the calculator.
If you wish, adjust the window on your calculator to make the intersection easier to see.

STEP 4   Find the point of intersection.

The calculator shows that the x-value for the point of intersection is 2.

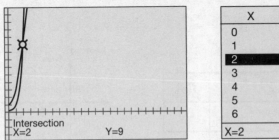

X	Y1	Y2
0	1	.11111
1	3	1
2	9	9
3	27	81
4	81	729
5	243	6561
6	729	59049

X=2

Intersection
X=2   Y=9

You can check your answer by using your calculator to look at the tables for the functions. Press 2nd   GRAPH .

The table shows that the y-values of both functions are equal when $x = 2$, so 2 is the solution.

SOLUTION $x = 2$

COACHED EXAMPLE

Solve $\left(\frac{1}{2}\right)^x = 2^{x-8}$.

THINKING IT THROUGH

Rewrite $\left(\frac{1}{2}\right)^x$ as a number with base 2 and a negative exponent.

$$\left(\frac{1}{2}\right)^x = \underline{\hspace{4cm}}$$

Rewrite each side of the equation so each has the same base, 2.

$2^{\underline{\hspace{0.8cm}}} = 2^{x-8}$

Use the one-to-one property to solve.

$\underline{\hspace{2cm}} = 2^{x-8}$ if and only if $\underline{\hspace{2cm}} = x - 8$.

Solve for x:

$\underline{\hspace{2cm}} = x - 8$

$\underline{\hspace{2cm}} = -8$

$\underline{\hspace{3cm}}$

The solution is $x = \underline{\hspace{1.5cm}}$.

Lesson Practice

Choose the correct answer.

1. What is the solution for $11^{3x-7} = 11^x$?

   A. $x = 7$ C. $x = 0$

   B. $x = \frac{7}{2}$ D. $x = -\frac{7}{2}$

2. What is the solution for $6^{x+2} = 216^x$?

   A. $x = -2$

   B. $x = 0$

   C. $x = 1$

   D. $x = \frac{1}{2}$

3. Cara drew the graph below to help her solve $2^x = -2$.

   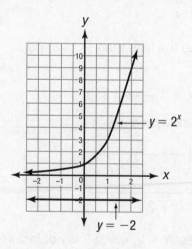

   Which conclusion should Cara draw based on her graph?

   A. The solution is $x = -1$.

   B. The solution is $x = 1$.

   C. The solution is the set of all real numbers.

   D. There is no solution.

4. What is the solution for $7^{2x+1} = 49$?

   A. $x = -1$

   B. $x = -\frac{1}{2}$

   C. $x = 0$

   D. $x = \frac{1}{2}$

5. What is the solution for $9^{5x} = 3^{3-2x}$?

   A. $x = \frac{1}{4}$

   B. $x = \frac{3}{7}$

   C. $x = -\frac{3}{7}$

   D. $x = -4$

6. What is the solution?

   $$7^x = 49^{x-2}$$

   A. $x = -4$

   B. $x = -2$

   C. $x = 2$

   D. $x = 4$

7. What is the solution?

   $$3^{1-2x} = 2{,}187$$

   A. $x = 7$

   B. $x = 3$

   C. $x = -3$

   D. $x = -7$

12 Solving Exponential Inequalities

MM2A2.d, MM2P1.c, MM2P1.d

You can solve exponential inequalities just as you solved exponential equations. The only difference is that you must keep the same inequality symbol that was in the original problem and, if necessary, remember to reverse the inequality symbol if you multiply or divide both sides by a negative number.

EXAMPLE 1

Solve: $16^x < 4^{x+1}$

STRATEGY   **Solve the inequality as you would solve an equation, but keep the less than (<) symbol.**

STEP 1   Are the bases the same?

No, the base on the left is 16 and the base on the right is 4.

STEP 2   Rewrite each side with the same base.

16 is a power of 4, so rewrite the left side.

$16^x < 4^{x+1} \longrightarrow (4^2)^x < 4^{x+1} \longrightarrow 4^{2x} < 4^{x+1}$

STEP 3   Rewrite the exponents as an inequality, keeping the less than (<) symbol.

$4^{2x} < 4^{x+1}$ is true if and only if $2x < x + 1$.

Use that fact to help you solve for x: $2x < x + 1 \longrightarrow x < 1$

STEP 4   Graph the solution. Test two values of x to check your answer.

Test: $x = 0$ $x = 2$

Test $x = 0$, since zero is included on the graph.	Test $x = 2$, since 2 is *not* included on the graph.
$16^0 \overset{?}{<} 4^{0+1}$	$16^2 \overset{?}{<} 4^{2+1}$
$1 < 4$	$16^2 \overset{?}{<} 4^3$
1 is less than 4, so 0 is a solution.	256 is not less than 64, so 2 is not a solution.

So, 0 is a solution and 2 is *not*. This matches the solution shown by the graph.

SOLUTION $x < 1$

You can also use graphing to solve exponential inequalities.

EXAMPLE 2

Solve: $2^{x+1} > 32$

STRATEGY   **Set each side of the equation equal to y. Graph the functions and find their point of intersection. Use that point to write an inequality.**

STEP 1   Set each side of the equation equal to y.

$y = 2^{x+1}$ and $y = 32$

STEP 2   Graph both functions on the same coordinate grid and label the points of intersection.

Make a table for $y = 2^{x+1}$. There is no need to make a table for $y = 32$, since its graph is a horizontal line.

x	$y = 2^{x+1}$	y
0	$y = 2^{0+1} = 2$	2
1	$y = 2^{1+1} = 4$	4
2	$y = 2^{2+1} = 8$	8
3	$y = 2^{3+1} = 16$	16
4	$y = 2^{4+1} = 32$	32
5	$y = 2^{5+1} = 64$	64

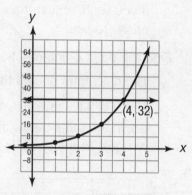

The two functions intersect when $x = 4$.

STEP 3   Choose the inequality symbol.

In the original inequality, $2^{x+1} > 32$, the inequality is true when the y-values for the function $y = 2^{x+1}$ are greater than 32. From the table or graph, you can see that the y-values are greater than 32 when $x > 4$.

SOLUTION $x > 4$

One final way to solve an exponential inequality is to use a graphing calculator. To review how to graph functions and find points of intersection on a calculator, look back at Lesson 7, Example 3, on page 52. To review how to see a table on a graphing calculator, look back at Lesson 11, Example 4, on page 76.

EXAMPLE 3

Solve: $6^{1-x} \leq 216$

STRATEGY   **Use a graphing calculator.**

STEP 1   Enter the expression on the left side of the equation as Y_1.

Enter: $Y_1 = 6^{1-x}$.

STEP 2   Enter the value on the right side of the equation as Y_2.

Enter: $Y_2 = 216$.

STEP 3   Graph the functions on the calculator.

If you wish, adjust the window on your calculator to make the intersection easier to see.

STEP 4   Find the point of intersection and write the inequality.

The calculator shows that the x-value for the point of intersection is -2.

The original inequality was $6^{1-x} \leq 216$.

So, in the table below, find the x-values for which the y_1-values are less than or equal to the y_2-values.

X	Y1	Y2
–3	1296	216
–2	216	216
–1	36	216
0	6	216
1	1	216
2	.16667	216
3	.02778	216

X=–2

The y_1-values are less than or equal to the y_2-values when $x \geq -2$.

SOLUTION $x \geq -2$

COACHED EXAMPLE

Solve: $2^{3x-10} \leq 4^4$

THINKING IT THROUGH

Rewrite each side with the same base.

4 is a power of 2, so rewrite the right side.

$4^4 =$ _____

Rewrite the original inequality so each side has a base of 2.

$2^{3x-10} \leq$ _____

You know that $2^{3x-10} \leq 2$ _____ if and only if $3x - 10 \leq$ _____.

Use that fact to solve for x:

$3x - 10 \leq$ _____

_____

_____

Graph the solution.

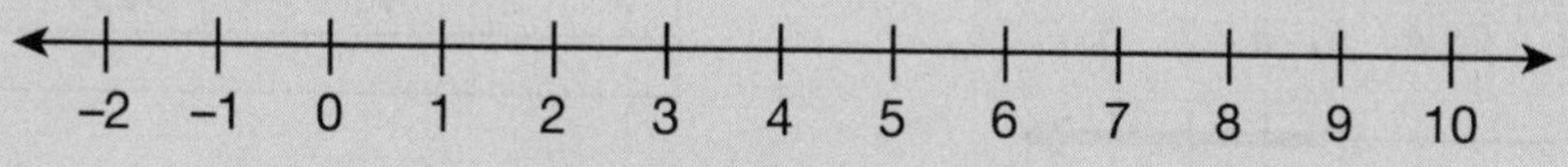

The solution is $x \leq$ _____ . Its graph is shown above.

Choose the correct answer.

1. What is the solution set for $6^{5x} < 6^{x-4}$?

   A. $x < -4$ C. $x > -1$

   B. $x < -1$ D. $x > -4$

2. What is the solution set for $7^{4x} \geq 49$?

   A. $x \leq -2$ C. $x \geq \frac{1}{2}$

   B. $x \leq \frac{1}{2}$ D. $x \geq 2$

3. Which graph shows the solution for $10^{x+3} > 10^5$?

   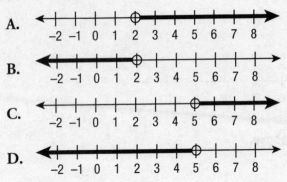

   A. (number line from −2 to 8, open circle at 2, shaded right)

   B. (number line from −2 to 8, open circle at 2, shaded left)

   C. (number line from −2 to 8, open circle at 5, shaded right)

   D. (number line from −2 to 8, open circle at 5, shaded left)

4. Gamal made this graph to help him solve $8^{x-3} \geq 64$.

   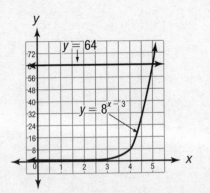

   What is the solution set of the inequality?

   A. $x \geq 5$ C. $x \leq 5$

   B. $x \geq 64$ D. $x \leq 64$

5. What is the solution set for $5^{9-x} < 625^{2x}$?

   A. $x > 1$

   B. $x > \frac{1}{3}$

   C. $x < \frac{1}{3}$

   D. $x < 3$

6. Sacha is using a graphing calculator correctly to solve $5^{x+6} > 125$.

	1	2
−6	1	125
−5	5	125
−4	25	125
−3	125	125
−2	625	125
−1	3125	125
0	15625	125

   Based on the table, what is the solution set for this inequality?

   A. $x > 125$

   B. $x > -3$

   C. $x < -3$

   D. $x < 125$

13 Transformations of Exponential Functions

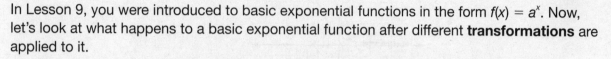

MM2A2.c

In Lesson 9, you were introduced to basic exponential functions in the form $f(x) = a^x$. Now, let's look at what happens to a basic exponential function after different **transformations** are applied to it.

The chart below explains how each type of transformation changes a function.

Transformation	Examples	
In a **vertical shift**, a graph of a function is translated either up or down on the coordinate plane.	$h(x) = a^x + 4$ $h(x) = a^x - k$	slide of 4 units *up* slide of *k* units *down*
In a **horizontal shift**, a graph of a function is translated either left or right on the coordinate plane.	$h(x) = a^{x+1}$ $h(x) = a^{x-h}$	slide of 1 unit *left* slide of *h* units *right*
In a **reflection**, a graph of a function is flipped over a line to form a mirror image.	$h(x) = -a^x$ $h(x) = a^{-x}$	across the *x*-axis across the *y*-axis
In a vertical **stretch**, the points of a graph are pulled vertically away from the *x*-axis. In a vertical **shrink**, they are pushed vertically toward the *x*-axis.	$h(x) = 5a^x$ $h(x) = \frac{1}{3}(a^x)$	stretched by 5 shrunk by $\frac{1}{3}$
In a horizontal stretch, the points of a graph are pulled horizontally away from the *y*-axis. In a horizontal shrink, they are pushed horizontally toward the *y*-axis.	$h(x) = a^{\frac{1}{2}x}$ $h(x) = a^{4x}$	stretched by 2 shrunk by $\frac{1}{4}$

EXAMPLE 1

On the graph below, draw the transformation of $f(x) = 2^x$ after a vertical shift of 4 units down. Write an equation for the new graph and describe its asymptote.

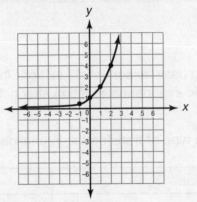

STRATEGY   Shift several points on the graph of $f(x) = 2^x$ 4 units down.

STEP 1   Identify several points on the graph of $f(x) = 2^x$.

For example, identify $(-1, 0.5)$, $(0, 1)$, $(1, 2)$, and $(2, 4)$.

STEP 2   Shift each of those points 4 units down.

$(-1, 0.5)$ moves to $(-1, -3.5)$.

$(0, 1)$ moves to $(0, -3)$.

$(1, 2)$ moves to $(1, -2)$.

$(2, 4)$ moves to $(2, 0)$.

Notice that the x-values stay the same, but the corresponding y-values decrease by 4. In other words, the new function $h(x) = f(x) - 4$, or $h(x) = 2^x - 4$.

STEP 3   Plot the new points, graph the transformation, and identify its asymptote.

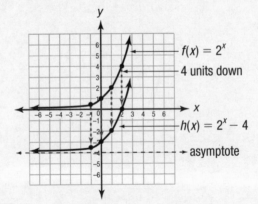

The graph of $f(x) = 2^x$ approaches, but never touches, the x-axis, so that is its asymptote.

The graph of $h(x) = 2^x - 4$ approaches, but never touches, $y = -4$, so that is its asymptote.

SOLUTION   The vertical shift of $f(x) = 2^x$ is shown in Step 3. Its asymptote is $y = -4$.

EXAMPLE 2

On the graph below, draw the reflection of $f(x) = 3^x$ across the y-axis. Write an equation for the new graph.

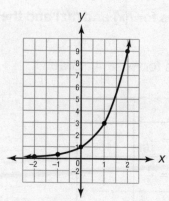

STRATEGY   **Find several points on the graph of $f(x) = 3^x$. Reflect those points across the y-axis.**

STEP 1   Choose several points on the graph of $f(x) = 3^x$.

For example, choose the points at $\left(-2, \frac{1}{9}\right)$, $\left(-1, \frac{1}{3}\right)$, $(0, 1)$, $(1, 3)$, and $(2, 9)$.

STEP 2   Reflect each of those points across the y-axis.

Each point and its reflection will be the same number of units from the y-axis. So, the y-values stay the same, but the sign of each x-value changes.

The image of $\left(-2, \frac{1}{9}\right)$ will be at $\left(2, \frac{1}{9}\right)$, and the image of $\left(-1, \frac{1}{3}\right)$ will be at $\left(1, \frac{1}{3}\right)$. $(0, 1)$ will be the same on both graphs.

The image of $(1, 3)$ will be at $(-1, 3)$, and the image of $(2, 9)$ will be at $(-2, 9)$.

STEP 3   Plot the new points and graph the transformation.

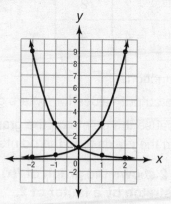

The new function can be represented as $h(x) = 3^{-x}$, or $h(x) = \frac{1}{3}x$.

SOLUTION   **The graph of $f(x) = 3^x$ and its reflected image, $h(x) = 3^{-x}$, are shown in Step 3.**

EXAMPLE 3

On a coordinate grid, draw the graph of $f(x) = 4^x$. Then draw a horizontal stretch of that function by a factor of 2 to form $h(x) = 4^{\frac{1}{2}x}$.

STRATEGY   **Make tables of values for $f(x)$ and $h(x)$ and then graph both functions. Compare them.**

STEP 1   Make a table of values for $f(x) = 4^x$. Graph it.

x	$f(x) = 4^x$	$f(x)$
−2	$f(-2) = 4^{-2} = \frac{1}{16}$	$\frac{1}{16}$
−1	$f(-1) = 4^{-1} = \frac{1}{4}$	$\frac{1}{4}$
0	$f(0) = 4^0 = 1$	1
1	$f(1) = 4^1 = 4$	4
2	$f(2) = 4^2 = 16$	16

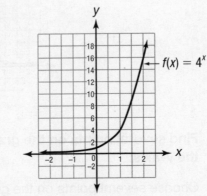

STEP 2   Make a table of values for $h(x) = 4^{\frac{1}{2}x}$. Graph it on the same grid.

x	$h(x) = 4^{\frac{1}{2}x}$	$h(x)$
−2	$h(-2) = 4^{\frac{1}{2} \cdot (-2)} = \frac{1}{4}$	$\frac{1}{4}$
−1	$h(-2) = 4^{\frac{1}{2} \cdot (-1)} = \frac{1}{2}$	$\frac{1}{2}$
0	$h(-2) = 4^{\frac{1}{2} \cdot 0} = 1$	1
1	$h(-2) = 4^{\frac{1}{2} \cdot 1} = 2$	2
2	$h(-2) = 4^{\frac{1}{2} \cdot 2} = 4$	4

STEP 3   Compare the two functions.

When $x > 0$, the output values for $f(x)$ are greater than the output values for $(h)x$.

This occurs because the points on the graph of $h(x)$ are pulled farther horizontally from the y-axis than the points on the graph of $f(x)$.

SOLUTION   **The graph in Step 2 shows the graph of $f(x) = 4^x$ and the graph of its image after a horizontal stretch by a factor of 2.**

COACHED EXAMPLE

Draw the transformation of $f(x) = \left(\frac{1}{2}\right)^x$ to $h(x) = \left(\frac{1}{2}\right)^{x-1}$.

Is the shift vertical or horizontal?

THINKING IT THROUGH

A graph of $f(x) = \left(\frac{1}{2}\right)^x$ is shown on the grid below. Draw the graph of $h(x) = \left(\frac{1}{2}\right)^{x-1}$ on the same grid.

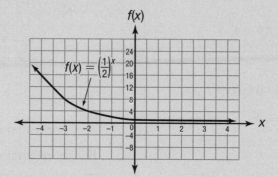

Look at the transformation you drew.

Did you shift the graph horizontally or vertically? _____

Above is the graph of $h(x) = \left(\frac{1}{2}\right)^{x-1}$, which is the result of a _____ shift of $f(x) = \left(\frac{1}{2}\right)^x$.

Lesson Practice

Choose the correct answer.

1. Which describes how the graph of $f(x) = 4^x$ was transformed to form the graph of $h(x) = \frac{1}{2}(4^x)$?

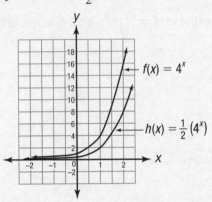

    A. vertical shift $\frac{1}{2}$ unit down of $f(x) = 4^x$

    B. vertical shift 2 units down of $f(x) = 4^x$

    C. vertical shrink by a factor of $\frac{1}{2}$ of $f(x) = 4^x$

    D. vertical stretch by a factor of 2 of $f(x) = 4^x$

2. Which describes how the graph of $f(x) = \left(\frac{1}{4}\right)^x$ was transformed to form the graph of $h(x) = -\left(\frac{1}{4}\right)^x$?

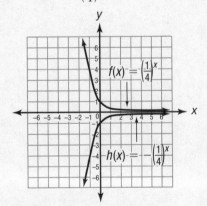

    A. reflection across the x-axis

    B. reflection across the y-axis

    C. vertical shift of 4 units down

    D. vertical shift of 4 units up

3. Which describes how the graph of $f(x) = 3^x$ was transformed to form the graph of $h(x) = 3^x + 3$?

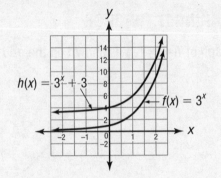

    A. horizontal shift of 3 units left

    B. horizontal shift of 3 units right

    C. vertical shift of 3 units down

    D. vertical shift of 3 units up

4. The graph of the function $f(x) = 10^x$ is transformed by a horizontal shift of 5 units to the left to form its image. Which equation represents the transformed image?

    A. $h(x) = 10^x - 5$

    B. $h(x) = 10^{x+5}$

    C. $h(x) = 10^{x-5}$

    D. $h(x) = 5(10^x)$

5. Which of the following coordinate grids shows a function, *f*, and its image, *h*, after a vertical shift of 1 unit up?

A.

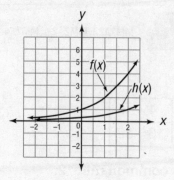

B.

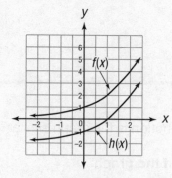

C.

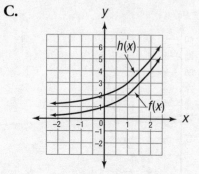

D.

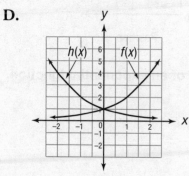

6. Which describes how the graph of $f(x) = 2^x$ was transformed to form the graph of $h(x) = 3(2^x)$?

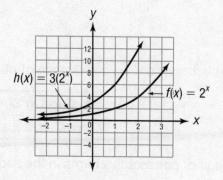

A. horizontal shrink of $f(x) = 2^x$ by a factor of $\frac{1}{3}$

B. horizontal stretch of $f(x) = 2^x$ by a factor of 3

C. vertical shrink of $f(x) = 2^x$ by a factor of $\frac{1}{3}$

D. vertical stretch of $f(x) = 2^x$ by a factor of 3

14 Geometric Sequences

MM2A2.f, MM2A2.g, MM2P4.a, MM2P4.b

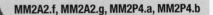

The table below shows a sequence of numbers.

Position in Sequence	1	2	3	4	5
Term	2	4	8	16	32

Each pair of consecutive terms in the sequence is related by the **common ratio**, 2.

$$\frac{4}{2} = \frac{8}{4} = \frac{16}{8} = \frac{32}{16} = 2$$

This is an example of a **geometric sequence**.

EXAMPLE 1

Plot the values in the table above on a graph. To which kind of function is the graph similar?

STRATEGY   **Plot the points in the table. Look at the shape of the graph.**

Plot the points (1, 2), (2, 4), (3, 8), (4, 16), and (5, 32).

The domain is only whole numbers, so the points should not be connected by a line. However, you can connect the points with a dashed line if it helps you see the shape of the graph better.

The curve looks like the graph of an exponential function.

SOLUTION   **The graph of the sequence looks like the graph of an exponential function.**

You can think of a geometric sequence as an exponential function whose domain is consecutive whole numbers greater than 0. The range is the consecutive terms of the sequence. We represent the terms of a sequence as $a_1, a_2, a_3, \ldots$

> The form for an exponential function is:
>
> $$f(x) = a^x, \text{ where } a \text{ is the base.}$$
>
> The formula for finding the nth term, a_n, in a geometric sequence is:
>
> $$a_n = a_1 \cdot r^{n-1}, \text{ where } r \text{ is the common ratio.}$$
>
> The common ratio, r, of the sequence, is raised to a power. So, r is like the base of an exponential function.

EXAMPLE 2

For a geometric sequence whose first term is 243, the common ratio is $\frac{1}{3}$. Write an equation that could be used to generate any term in the function. Then use that equation to graph the first five terms in the sequence.

STRATEGY   Write an equation using the formula for finding the nth term, a_n, in a geometric sequence. Then graph the points.

STEP 1   Use the formula to write an equation.

first term $= a_1 = 243 \qquad r = \frac{1}{3}$

$$a_1 \cdot r^{n-1} = 243 \cdot \left(\frac{1}{3}\right)^{n-1}$$

STEP 2   Make a table of values and plot the points.

n	$a_n = 243 \cdot \left(\frac{1}{3}\right)^{n-1}$	a_n
1	$a_1 = 243 \cdot \left(\frac{1}{3}\right)^{1-1} = 243$	243
2	$a_2 = 243 \cdot \left(\frac{1}{3}\right)^{2-1} = 81$	81
3	$a_3 = 243 \cdot \left(\frac{1}{3}\right)^{3-1} = 27$	27
4	$a_4 = 243 \cdot \left(\frac{1}{3}\right)^{4-1} = 9$	9
5	$a_5 = 243 \cdot \left(\frac{1}{3}\right)^{5-1} = 3$	3

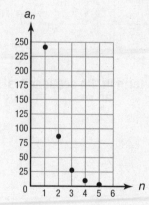

SOLUTION   **The table and graph show the first five terms in the sequence: 243, 81, 27, 9, and 3.**

EXAMPLE 3

Find the 8th term of this geometric sequence: 5, 20, 80, …

STRATEGY   **Use the first three terms to find the common ratio. Then apply the formula to find the 8th term.**

STEP 1   Find the ratio between any two consecutive terms, the common ratio.

$$r = \frac{20}{5} = 4$$

STEP 2   Use the formula to find the 8th term.

$$a_n = a_1 \cdot r^{n-1}$$
$$a_8 = 5 \cdot 4^{8-1} = 5 \cdot 4^7 = 81{,}920$$

SOLUTION   **The 8th term is 81,920.**

COACHED EXAMPLE

Find the 6th term of a geometric sequence whose first term is 1,000 and whose common ratio is 1.5.

THINKING IT THROUGH

You need to find the 6th term, so n is equal to 6.

The first term, or a_1, is equal to _____.

The common ratio, or r, is equal to _____.

Substitute those values into the formula and find the 6th term.

$$a_n = a_1 \cdot r^{n-1}$$
$$a_6 = \underline{\hspace{2cm}} \cdot (\underline{\hspace{2cm}})^{6-1}$$
$$= \underline{\hspace{3cm}}$$

The 6th term in the sequence is _____.

Lesson Practice

Choose the correct answer.

1. The first three terms of a geometric sequence are shown below. What is the 5th term of the sequence?

$$10, 70, 490, \dots$$

   A. 610

   B. 3,430

   C. 24,010

   D. 168,070

2. This equation can be used to find the nth term in a geometric sequence.

$$a_n = a_1 \cdot r^{n-1}$$

   This equation is an example of an exponential function. Which variable in the equation could be interpreted as the base of the exponential function?

   A. a_n

   B. a_1

   C. n

   D. r

Use this information for questions 3–5.

The first term in a geometric sequence is -1 and it has a common ratio of 7.

3. Which equation represents the nth term in the sequence?

   A. $-1 \cdot 7^{n-1}$

   B. $-1 \cdot 7^{n+1}$

   C. $7 \cdot -1^n$

   D. $7 \cdot -1^{n-1}$

4. What are the first three terms in the sequence?

   A. 7, 49, 343

   B. 1, 7, 49

   C. $-1, -7, -49$

   D. $-7, -49, -343$

5. What is the 5th term in the sequence?

   A. $-16,807$

   B. $-2,401$

   C. -7

   D. 343

6. To find terms in a particular geometric sequence, this equation can be used:

$$a_n = 35 \cdot 2^{n-1}$$

This equation is an exponential function. Which best describes the domain for that function?

A. the set of all real numbers

B. the set of all integers

C. the set of consecutive whole numbers greater than 0

D. the set of consecutive whole numbers greater than 1 and less than 100

7. A geometric sequence whose first term is 64 has a common ratio of $\frac{1}{4}$. Which equation represents the nth term in the sequence?

A. $\frac{1}{4} \cdot 64^n$

B. $\frac{1}{4} \cdot 64^{n-1}$

C. $64 \cdot \left(\frac{1}{4}\right)^n$

D. $64 \cdot \left(\frac{1}{4}\right)^{n-1}$

8. The first three terms of a geometric sequence are shown below. What is the 10th term of the sequence?

2, 8, 32, …

A. 524,288

B. 131,072

C. 32,768

D. 128

9. A sequence is graphed below.

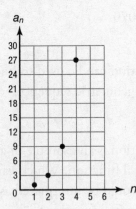

Which equation represents this sequence?

A. $a_n = 1 \cdot 3^n$

B. $a_n = 1 \cdot 3^{n-1}$

C. $a_n = 2 \cdot 3^{n-1}$

D. $a_n = 3 \cdot 2^{n-1}$

1. A piecewise function is shown below.

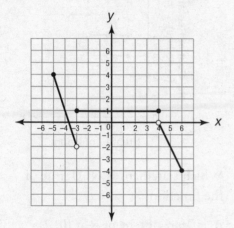

Which is true of this piecewise function?

A. The function is continuous.

B. The function is decreasing on the interval $\{-2 \leq x \leq 4\}$.

C. The function is constant on the interval $\{-3 \leq x \leq 4\}$.

D. The function is increasing on the interval $\{4 < x \leq 6\}$.

2. Which graph best represents the solution of $|3x| + 1 < 4$?

A. ![number line A with closed dots at -1 and 1](shading between -1 and 1)
   -5 -4 -3 -2 -1 0 1 2 3 4 5

B. ![number line B with closed dots at -1 and 1](shading between -1 and 1)
   -5 -4 -3 -2 -1 0 1 2 3 4 5

C. ![number line C with open circles at -1 and 1](shading outside -1 and 1)
   -5 -4 -3 -2 -1 0 1 2 3 4 5

D. ![number line D with open circles at -1 and 1](shading between -1 and 1)
   -5 -4 -3 -2 -1 0 1 2 3 4 5

Use this graph of an absolute value function for questions 3 and 4.

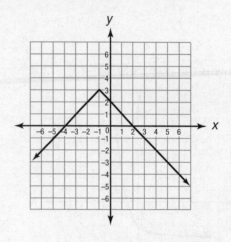

3. How could this function be written as a piecewise function?

A. $f(x) = \begin{cases} x + 4, \text{ if } x < -1 \\ -x + 2, \text{ if } x \geq -1 \end{cases}$

B. $f(x) = \begin{cases} x + 4, \text{ if } x < -1 \\ -x - 2, \text{ if } x \geq -1 \end{cases}$

C. $f(x) = \begin{cases} x + 4, \text{ if } x < 0 \\ -x + 2, \text{ if } x \geq 0 \end{cases}$

D. $f(x) = \begin{cases} x + 4, \text{ if } x < 0 \\ -x - 2, \text{ if } x \geq 0 \end{cases}$

4. Which statement is true of the function above?

A. The minimum is 3.

B. The vertex is at $(-1, 3)$.

C. The axis of symmetry is the y-axis.

D. The range is the set of all real numbers.

5. What is the solution for $2^{6-4x} > 16$?

A. $x < -\dfrac{1}{2}$

B. $x < \dfrac{1}{2}$

C. $x > \dfrac{1}{2}$

D. $x > -\dfrac{1}{2}$

6. Below is the graph of $f(x) = 3^x - 3$.

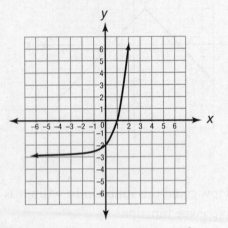

Which statement is NOT true of this function?

A. The point at $(0, -2)$ is a y-intercept.

B. The point at $(1, 0)$ is an x-intercept.

C. The function has no zeros.

D. The function will increase without bound as x approaches infinity.

7. The cost of skate rental at an ice rink for up to 5 hours is represented by the piecewise function graphed below.

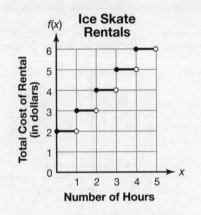

Which statement is NOT true of the function?

A. The y-intercept is at $(0, 2)$.

B. The function is continuous.

C. The minimum cost if one rents skates is 2 dollars.

D. The range is the set of integers on the interval $\{2 \le x \le 6\}$.

8. Pedro uses this equation to find the *n*th term in a geometric sequence.

$$a_n = 3 \cdot 4^{n-1}$$

Pedro recognizes this sequence as an exponential function. Which number or variable in the equation could be interpreted as the base of the exponential function?

A. a_n

B. n

C. 3

D. 4

9. Which coordinate grid below shows a function, *f*, and its image, *h*, after a reflection across the *y*-axis?

A.

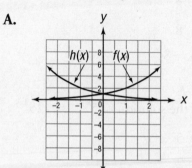

B.

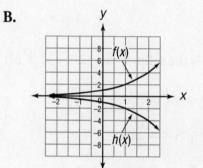

C.

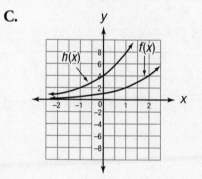

D.

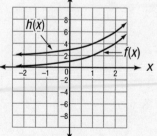

10. What is the solution set for $2|x - 1| = 14$?

A. 6, 8

B. 6, −8

C. −6, 8

D. −6, −8

11. What is the solution of $5^{x+1} = 125^{2x}$?

A. $x = 5$

B. $x = 2$

C. $x = 1$

D. $x = \dfrac{1}{5}$

12. What is the solution for $|2x - 3| \geq 6$?

A. $x \leq -\dfrac{3}{2}$ or $x \geq \dfrac{9}{2}$

B. $-\dfrac{3}{2} \leq x \leq \dfrac{9}{2}$

C. $x \leq -\dfrac{9}{2}$ or $x \geq \dfrac{3}{2}$

D. $-\dfrac{9}{2} \leq x \leq \dfrac{3}{2}$

13. A single bacterium is dropped into a glass of milk. Every hour, the number of bacteria in the milk quadruples, as represented by the function $f(x) = 4^x$. Which graph best represents this function?

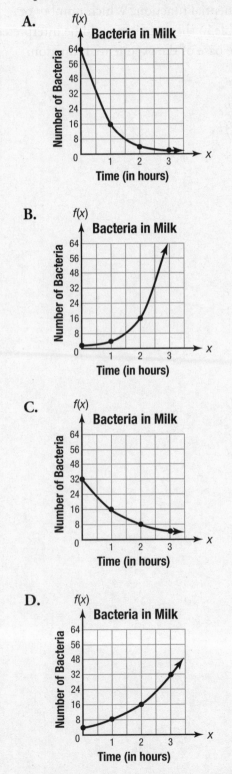

OPEN-ENDED QUESTION

14. The first five terms of a geometric sequence are: 5, 10, 20, 40, 80.

Think of this sequence as an exponential function.

A.   Plot the first five terms as ordered pairs (n, a_n) on the graph below, but do not connect them.

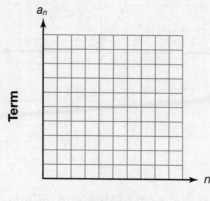

Explain why the points above should not be connected. What does this mean about the domain of the exponential function that represents this sequence?

_____

_____

_____

B.   What is the common ratio, r, for the sequence? Explain how you found your answer.
Common ratio: _____

_____

_____

C.   Write an equation that could be used to find the nth term, a_n, in this sequence. (Be sure to describe any variables you use.) Then use that equation to find the 10th term in the sequence. Show your work.
Equation: $a_n =$ _____

10th term: _____

15. The function $f(x) = \left(\frac{1}{2}\right)^x$ is graphed below.

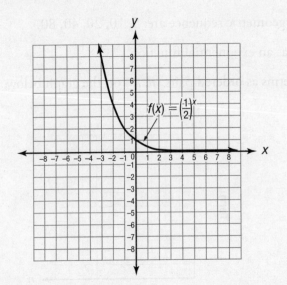

$f(x) = \left(\frac{1}{2}\right)^x$

A. What is the asymptote of $f(x) = \left(\frac{1}{2}\right)^x$? Label it on the grid above. Explain what an asymptote is and how you know the line you chose is the asymptote of $f(x)$.

asymptote of $f(x)$: _____

_____

_____

_____

B. Transform $f(x) = \left(\frac{1}{2}\right)^x$ with a vertical shift of 3 units down to form $h(x) = \left(\frac{1}{2}\right)^x - 3$. Graph and label the transformation on the grid above.

C. What is the asymptote of $h(x) = \left(\frac{1}{2}\right)^x - 3$? Label it on the grid above. How did the transformation affect the asymptote?

asymptote of $h(x)$: _____

_____

_____

_____

CHAPTER 3

Quadratics and Inverses of Functions

15 Characteristics of Quadratic Functions

MM2A3.a, MM2A3.c, MM2P1.b, MM2P3.a, MM2P3.d

A **quadratic function** is a function in which the greatest power of any variable is 2. The **standard form** of a quadratic function is: $f(x) = ax^2 + bx + c$, in which a, b, and c are real numbers and $a \neq 0$.

The graph of a quadratic function is always a U-shaped curve called a parabola.

You can determine a lot about a quadratic function from its equation, even without looking at its graph.

> For a function in the form $f(x) = ax^2 + bx + c$:
>
> - The axis of symmetry is the vertical line $x = \frac{-b}{2a}$.
> - The vertex is at the point $\left(\frac{-b}{2a}, f\left(\frac{-b}{2a}\right) \right)$.
> - The y-intercept is at $(0, c)$.

Many of the characteristics of piecewise functions and exponential functions discussed in Lessons 6 and 10 are also characteristics of quadratic functions.

EXAMPLE 1

Below is the graph of $f(x) = x^2 - 4x + 3$, with a restricted domain. Identify the domain, range, intercepts, zeros, and intervals of increase and decrease for this function.

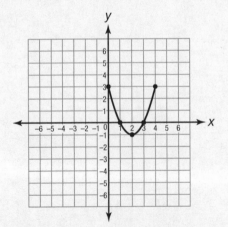

STRATEGY   Use the definitions of domain, range, intercepts, and zeros.

STEP 1   Identify the domain and the range.

The domain includes all the x-values. The least x-value is 0 and the greatest is 4. The domain is $0 \leq x \leq 4$.

The range includes all the y-values or $f(x)$-values. The least $f(x)$-value is -1 and the greatest is 3. The range is $-1 \leq y \leq 3$.

STEP 2   Identify the intercepts.

The graph crosses the x-axis at (1, 0) and (3, 0), so those are the x-intercepts.

The graph crosses the y-axis at (0, 3), so that is the y-intercept.

You could also determine this from the equation.

In the equation, $f(x) = x^2 - 4x + 3$, $c = 3$. The y-intercept is at (0, c), or (0, 3).

STEP 3   Identify the zeros.

The zeros of a function are any values of x that make $f(x) = 0$.

Looking at the x-intercepts, you can see that the y-value is 0 when the x-values are 1 and 3.

Use the equation to check that those values make $f(x) = 0$.

Test $x = 1$.	Test $x = 3$.
$f(x) = (1)^2 - 4(1) + 3 = 0$	$f(x) = (3)^2 - 4(3) + 3 = 0$

Both of those values make $f(x) = 0$, so the zeros are 1 and 3.

STEP 4   Identify the intervals of increase and decrease.

Remember, use x-values to identify intervals of increase and decrease.

The function is decreasing on the interval $\{0 \leq x < 2\}$.

The function is increasing on the interval $\{2 < x \leq 4\}$.

SOLUTION   **The domain is $0 \leq x \leq 4$. The range is $-1 \leq y \leq 3$. The y-intercept is at (0, 3). The x-intercepts are at (1, 0) and (3, 0). The zeros of the function are 1 and 3. The function is decreasing on the interval $\{0 \leq x < 2\}$ and is increasing on the interval $\{2 < x \leq 4\}$.**

Quadratic functions can also be written in **vertex form**: $f(x) = a(x - h)^2 + k$, where $a \neq 0$. The vertex form provides information about certain characteristics of the function.

> For a function in the form $f(x) = a(x - h)^2 + k$:
> - The vertex is at (h, k).
> - The axis of symmetry is the line $x = h$. The axis of symmetry passes through the vertex and divides the parabola into two congruent halves.
> - The values of a and k tell you about the extrema (the maximum and minimum).
>
> If a is positive, then k is the minimum and both arms of the graph point up.
> If a is negative, then k is the maximum and both arms point down.

EXAMPLE 2

Identify the extrema, the vertex, and the axis of symmetry for the function graphed on the right.

Then write an equation for the function in vertex form.

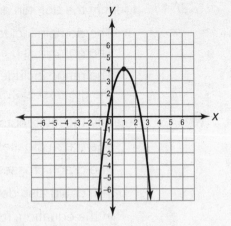

STRATEGY Use the definitions of maximum, minimum, vertex, and axis of symmetry. Then use the vertex form to write the quadratic equation.

STEP 1 Does the graph have a minimum or a maximum?

The arms of the graph point down and extend toward negative infinity, so the graph has a maximum, but no minimum. The maximum is 4.

STEP 2 Label the vertex and the axis of symmetry on the graph.

The vertex is at the maximum, so the vertex is at (1, 4).

The axis of symmetry, $x = 1$, passes through the vertex and divides the function into two congruent halves.

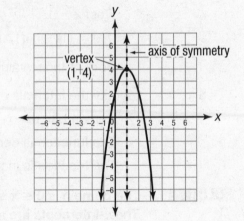

STEP 3 Write an equation for the graph.

The vertex is at (1, 4). So, substitute 1 for h and 4 for k into the vertex form:

$$f(x) = a(x - h)^2 + k = a(x - 1)^2 + 4$$

Notice that the graph passes through (0, 2). This means that $f(0) = 2$. Use those values to solve for a.

$$2 = a(0 - 1)^2 + 4$$

$$2 = a + 4$$

$$-2 = a$$

The equation is $f(x) = -2(x - 1)^2 + 4$.

SOLUTION The maximum is 4. The vertex is at (1, 4). The axis of symmetry is $x = 1$. In vertex form, the equation for this graph is $f(x) = -2(x - 1)^2 + 4$.

Sometimes, you may need to convert between standard and vertex forms.

EXAMPLE 3

Convert $2x^2 - 8x + 7$ to vertex form.

STRATEGY   **Use what you know about equations written in standard form, $ax^2 + bx + c$.**

STEP 1   Use algebra to find the vertex.

In $2x^2 - 8x + 7$, $a = 2$, $b = -8$, and $c = 7$.

The vertex is at $\left(\frac{-b}{2a}, f\left(\frac{-b}{2a}\right)\right)$. Find those values.

$\frac{-b}{2a} = \frac{-(-8)}{2 \cdot 2} = \frac{-(-8)}{4} = \frac{8}{4} = 2$

$f\left(\frac{-b}{2a}\right) = f(2) = 2x^2 - 8x + 7 = 2(2^2) - 8(2) + 7 = 8 - 16 + 7 = -1$

The vertex is at $(2, -1)$.

STEP 2   Write the equation in vertex form.

The vertex is at $(2, -1)$. Substitute 2 for h and -1 for k into the vertex form of a quadratic function. Since you know that $a = 2$, substitute that as well:

$f(x) = a(x - h)^2 + k = 2(x - 2)^2 - 1$

SOLUTION   **The vertex form is $f(x) = 2(x - 2)^2 - 1$.**

Since the graph of a quadratic function is a U-shaped curve, its rate of change varies.

EXAMPLE 4

A projectile was shot upward from the ground with an initial speed of 96 feet per second. The height of the projectile at any given time can be represented by the function $f(x) = 96x - 16x^2$. The graph below represents this function. Briefly describe the rate of change for this function.

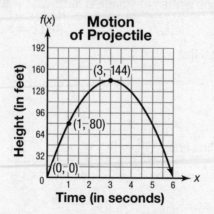

STRATEGY   **Use what you know about slopes to interpret the rate of change.**

STEP 1   Find the average rate of change (slope) between different points on the graph.

Since the graph is not a straight line, the change in the height depends on the values of x used.

The average rate of change between (0, 0), and (1, 80) is:

$$m = \frac{y_2 - y_1}{x_2 - x_1} = \frac{80 - 0}{1 - 0} = \frac{80}{1} = 80 \text{ feet per second.}$$

The average rate of change between (1, 80), and (2, 128) is:

$$m = \frac{y_2 - y_1}{x_2 - x_1} = \frac{128 - 80}{2 - 1} = 48 = 48 \text{ feet per second.}$$

So, as the height of the projectile increases, its rate of change decreases. The slopes are positive between 0 and 3 seconds, indicating that the height of the ball increases for 3 seconds.

STEP 2   Examine the rest of the graph.

At (3, 144), the projectile reaches its maximum height. At that point, its height is neither increasing nor decreasing. So, its rate of change is 0.

After that, the curve moves downward from left to right, so the slopes become negative and the height decreases. The projectile falls slowly at first and then picks up speed as it approaches the ground.

SOLUTION   **This function has a variable rate of change. The rate of change is positive until the ball reaches its maximum height, 144 feet. The rate of change is 0 at (3, 144). The rate of change is negative as the ball falls to the ground.**

COACHED EXAMPLE

Identify the axis of symmetry, vertex, and y-intercept for the function $f(x) = x^2 + 6x - 8$.

THINKING IT THROUGH

Use what you know about equations written in standard form, $ax^2 + bx + c$.

In $f(x) = 2x^2 + 12x - 16$, $a =$ _____, $b =$ _____, and $c =$ _____.

The axis of symmetry is the vertical line $x = \frac{-b}{2a}$.

The axis of symmetry is: $x = \frac{-b}{2a} =$ _____.

The vertex is at $\left(\frac{-b}{2a}, f\left(\frac{-b}{2a}\right)\right)$.

You already know the x-value of the vertex, $\frac{-b}{2a}$, which is _____.

Find the $f(x)$-value: _____

The vertex is at (_____, _____).

The y-intercept is c.

The y-intercept is at (0, _____).

Lesson Practice

Choose the correct answer.

1. Below is the graph of $f(x) = -2x^2 - 4x$.

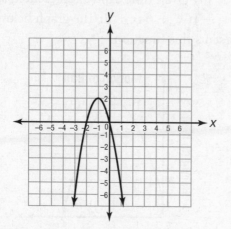

Which of the following statements is **not** true?

A. The range is the set of all real numbers less than or equal to 2.

B. The function is increasing on the interval $\{-\infty < x < -1\}$.

C. The zeros are -1 and 0.

D. The vertex is at $(-1, 2)$.

2. Which shows $f(x) = -\frac{1}{2}(x - 4)^2 - 3$ in standard form?

A. $f(x) = -\frac{1}{2}x^2 + 4x - 11$

B. $f(x) = -\frac{1}{2}x^2 - 4x + 5$

C. $f(x) = \frac{1}{4}x^2 - 2x + 4$

D. $f(x) = \frac{1}{4}x^2 - 2x + 1$

3. A small manufacturer of lawn tractors has daily production costs of $C(x) = 0.5x^2 - 10x + 900$, where C is the total cost in dollars and x is the number of units produced. The graph below shows this situation.

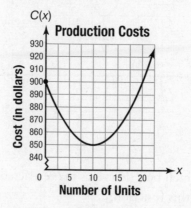

Which statement is true?

A. The minimum daily cost is $900.

B. The minimum daily cost is $850.

C. If the manufacturer keeps the daily cost to a minimum, 5 units will be manufactured that day.

D. If the manufacturer keeps the daily cost to a minimum, 20 units will be manufactured that day.

4. What is the axis of symmetry of the function $f(x) = 10x^2 - 11x - 3$?

A. $x = \frac{11}{10}$

B. $x = \frac{11}{20}$

C. $x = -\frac{11}{20}$

D. $x = -3$

Use this graph for questions 5 and 6.

Below is the graph of $f(x) = x^2 + 2x + 6$, with a restricted domain.

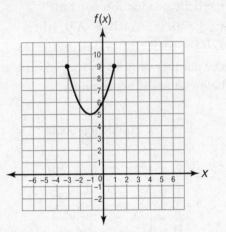

Use this information for questions 7 and 8.

A ball was shot upward by a machine that was several feet above the ground with an initial speed of 64 feet per second. The height of the ball at any given time can be represented as $f(x) = -16x^2 + 64x + 8$. The graph below represents this function.

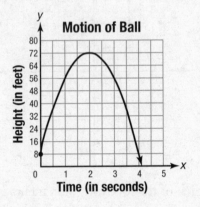

5. Which best describes the restricted domain of this function?

    A. the set of all integers

    B. the set of all real numbers greater than or equal to -3

    C. the set of all real numbers greater than or equal to 5 and less than or equal to 9

    D. the set of all real numbers greater than or equal to -3 and less than or equal to 1

6. Which statement is **not** true?

    A. It has an x-intercept at $(0, 6)$.

    B. Its minimum is at $(-1, 5)$.

    C. Its maximum is 9.

    D. It is decreasing on the interval $\{-3 \leq x < -1\}$.

7. For which of these times is the rate of change positive?

    A. between 0 and 2 seconds

    B. only at 2 seconds

    C. between 2 and 4 seconds

    D. only after 4 seconds

8. The y-intercept is at $(0, 8)$. What does the y-intercept represent in this situation?

    A. the time it takes the ball to reach the ground, 8 seconds

    B. the maximum height the ball reaches in the air, 8 feet

    C. the height from which the ball is shot upward, 8 feet

    D. the speed of the ball, 8 feet per second

16 Transformations of Quadratic Functions

MM2A3.b, MM2P2.b, MM2P2.c, MM2P3.b

Just as you transformed exponential functions in Lesson 13, you can also transform quadratic functions. In fact, the graph of any quadratic function can be thought of as a transformation of the basic quadratic function $f(x) = x^2$.

EXAMPLE 1

The function $f(x) = x^2$ is graphed on the right. Graph and describe its transformation, $h(x) = (x - 2)^2$. Then compare the equations of the two functions and make a conjecture about those equations.

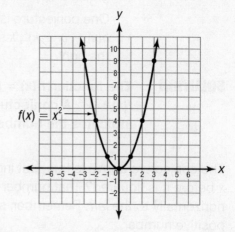

STRATEGY   **Make a table of values for $h(x)$. Then graph the function and describe the transformation.**

STEP 1   Make a table of values for $h(x) = (x - 2)^2$.

Choose several x-values. You may need to try a number of values to find ordered pairs that will fit on a coordinate grid with a y-axis from -2 to 10.

x	$h(x) = (x - 2)^2$	$h(x)$
-2	$h(-2) = (-2 - 2)^2 = 16$	$16 \rightarrow$ won't fit on grid
-1	$h(-1) = (-1 - 2)^2 = 9$	9
0	$h(0) = (0 - 2)^2 = 4$	4
1	$h(1) = (1 - 2)^2 = 1$	1
2	$h(2) = (2 - 2)^2 = 0$	0
3	$h(3) = (3 - 2)^2 = 1$	1
4	$h(4) = (4 - 2)^2 = 4$	4
5	$h(5) = (5 - 2)^2 = 9$	9

STEP 2 Graph $h(x) = (x - 2)^2$ and describe the transformation.

Each point on the graph of $f(x)$ is shifted 2 units to the right to form $h(x)$. So, the transformation is a horizontal shift of 2 units right.

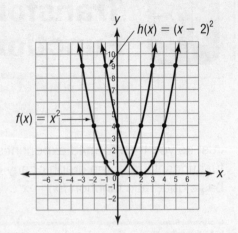

STEP 3 Compare the two equations and make a conjecture about them.

In $f(x)$, x is squared. In $h(x)$, $(x - 2)$ is squared, so 2 is subtracted from x before it is squared.

The graph of $h(x)$ is 2 units to the right of the graph of $f(x)$.

One conjecture is that when a function in the form $f(x) = x^2$ is transformed to $h(x) = (x - k)^2$, k shows the number of units the function shifts horizontally to the right.

SOLUTION **The function $h(x) = (x - 2)^2$ is a horizontal shift of 2 units to the right of $f(x) = x^2$. A conjecture is that the number subtracted from x before it is squared indicates the number of units the graph shifts to the right.**

The conjecture above is true, but incomplete. What if a negative number is subtracted from x before it is squared? That number would indicate the number of units the function shifts horizontally to the *left*. Remember, subtracting a negative number is the same as adding a positive number.

The chart below summarizes how vertical shifts, horizontal shifts, and reflections change the basic quadratic function $f(x) = x^2$.

Transformation	Examples of Transformations of $f(x) = x^2$	
Vertical shift	$h(x) = x^2 + 1$	slide of 1 unit *up*
	$h(x) = x^2 - k$	slide of k units *down*
Horizontal shift	$h(x) = (x + 5)^2$	slide of 5 units *left*
	$h(x) = (x - k)^2$	slide of k units *right*
Reflection	$h(x) = -x^2$	across the x-axis
	$h(x) = (-x)^2 = x^2$	across the y-axis

EXAMPLE 2

What is the result when the function $f(x) = x^2$ is reflected across the y-axis?

STRATEGY   **Use the graph of $f(x) = x^2$ from Example 1. Then graph the transformation of $f(x)$ after the reflection.**

     STEP 1   Identify several points on the graph of $f(x) = x^2$.

         $(-3, 9)$, $(-2, 4)$, $(0, 0)$, $(1, 1)$ and $(3, 9)$

     STEP 2   Identify the reflections of those points across the y-axis.

         The reflection of $(-3, 9)$ is $(3, 9)$.

         The reflection of $(-2, 4)$ is $(2, 4)$.

         The point at $(0, 0)$ is the same on both graphs.

         The reflection of $(1, 1)$ is $(-1, 1)$.

         The reflection of $(3, 9)$ is $(-3, 9)$.

     STEP 3   Graph $h(x) = (-x)^2$ (the reflection over the y-axis) on a different coordinate grid and compare it to the graph of $f(x) = x^2$.

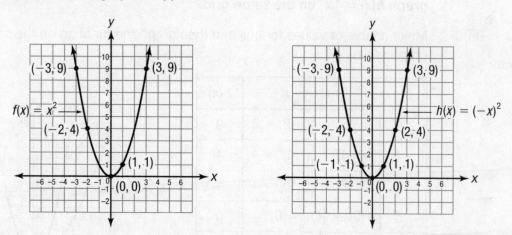

     STEP 4   What do you notice about the graph of $f(x)$ and its image after a reflection over the y-axis?

         The two graphs are identical. So, the function $f(x)$ is its own reflection across the y-axis.

SOLUTION   **When you reflect $f(x) = x^2$ across the y-axis, the reflected image is identical to the original graph.**

A vertical stretch pulls the points of a graph away from the x-axis. A vertical shrink pushes the points of a graph toward the x-axis. In a vertical stretch or a vertical shrink, the factor of x^2 determines the amount of stretch or shrink that is applied to the graph of $f(x) = x^2$.

- A vertical stretch ($c > 1$) and a vertical shrink ($c < 1$) change the graph by a factor of c, $c \cdot f(x)$.

A horizontal stretch pulls the points of a graph away from the y-axis. A horizontal shrink pushes the points of a graph toward the y-axis. In a horizontal stretch or a horizontal shrink, the coefficient of x determines the amount of stretch or shrink that is applied to the graph of $f(x) = x^2$.

- A horizontal stretch ($c < 1$) and a horizontal shrink ($c > 1$) change the graph by a factor of $\frac{1}{c}$, $f(c \cdot x)$.

Remember, when c has a negative value the graph will be reflected over an axis.

EXAMPLE 3

Transform $f(x) = x^2$ with a shrink to form $h(x) = \frac{1}{4}x^2$. Was the shrink horizontal or vertical?

STRATEGY **Use the graph of $f(x) = x^2$ from Example 1. Then make a table of values and graph $h(x) = \frac{1}{4}x^2$ on the same grid.**

STEP 1 Make a table of values for $h(x)$ and then graph the function on the same grid as the graph of $f(x)$.

x	$h(x) = \frac{1}{4}x^2$	$h(x)$
−6	$h(-6) = \frac{1}{4}(-6)^2 = 9$	9
−4	$h(-4) = \frac{1}{4}(-4)^2 = 4$	4
−2	$h(-2) = \frac{1}{4}(-2)^2 = 1$	1
0	$h(0) = \frac{1}{4}(0)^2 = 0$	0
2	$h(2) = \frac{1}{4}(2)^2 = 1$	1
4	$h(4) = \frac{1}{4}(4)^2 = 4$	4
6	$h(6) = \frac{1}{4}(6)^2 = 9$	9

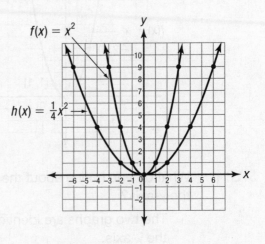

STEP 2 Describe the shrink.

The points of the graph of h are pushed closer to the x-axis. For example, in f, when $x = -2$, $f(x) = 4$. In h, when $x = -2$, $h(x) = 1$. The point on the graph of h, $(-2, 1)$, is closer to the x-axis than the point on the graph of f, $(-2, 4)$.

Because the points are pushed closer to the x-axis, this is a vertical shrink.

The equation is $h(x) = \frac{1}{4}x^2$, so the factor is $\frac{1}{4}$.

SOLUTION **The graph under Step 1 shows the result of a vertical shrink of $f(x) = x^2$ by a factor of $\frac{1}{4}$.**

COACHED EXAMPLE

Transform $f(x) = x^2$ with a stretch to form $h(x) = 3x^2$. Describe the stretch.

THINKING IT THROUGH

A graph of $f(x) = x^2$ is shown on the grid below.

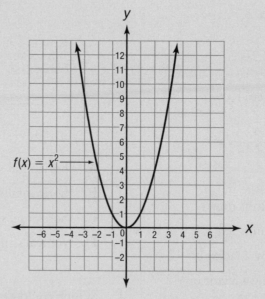

Make a table of values for $h(x)$.

x	$h(x) = 3x^2$	$h(x)$
−2	$h(-2) = 3 \cdot (-2)^2 = 12$	12
−1	$h(-1) =$	
0	$h(0) =$	
1	$h(1) =$	
2	$h(2) =$	

Graph those points on the grid above. Look at the transformation you drew.

In a vertical stretch, the points of a graph are pulled vertically away from the _____-axis.

In a horizontal stretch, the points of a graph are pulled horizontally away from the _____-axis.

Which of those describes how *f* was transformed to *h*? _____

Above is the graph of $h(x) = 3x^2$, which is the result of a _____ stretch of $f(x) = x^2$.

Lesson Practice

Choose the correct answer.

1. Which describes how the graph of $f(x) = x^2$ was transformed to form the graph of $h(x) = x^2 - 2$?

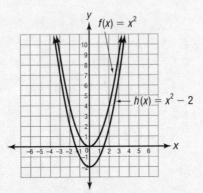

A. vertical shift of $f(x)$ 2 units down

B. vertical shift of $f(x)$ 2 units left

C. vertical shrink of $f(x)$ by a factor of -2

D. vertical stretch of $f(x)$ by a factor of -2

2. Which describes how the graph of $f(x) = x^2$ was transformed to form the graph of $h(x) = -x^2$?

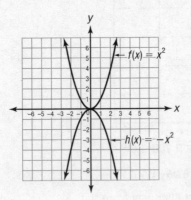

A. reflection across the x-axis

B. reflection across the y-axis

C. vertical shift of 1 unit down

D. vertical shift of 4 units down

3. Which describes how the graph of $f(x) = x^2$ was transformed to form the graph of $h(x) = (x + 4)^2$?

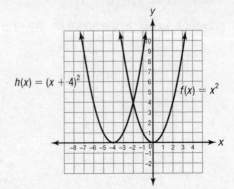

A. horizontal shift of $f(x)$ 4 units right

B. horizontal shift of $f(x)$ 4 units left

C. horizontal stretch of $f(x)$ by a factor of 4

D. vertical shift of $f(x)$ 4 units up

4. Which could describe how the graph of $f(x) = x^2$ was transformed to form the graph of $h(x) = -2x^2$ in two steps?

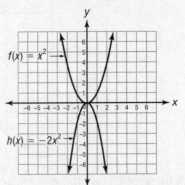

A. reflection across the x-axis followed by a vertical shift of 2 units up

B. reflection across the y-axis followed by a vertical shift of 2 units down

C. reflection across the x-axis followed by a vertical stretch by a factor of 2

D. reflection across the y-axis followed by a vertical stretch by a factor of 2

17 Arithmetic Series

MM2A3.d, MM2A3.e, MM2P4.a, MM2P4.b

Take a look at this sequence: 2, 4, 6, 8, 10, … Each pair of consecutive terms differs by the same number, 2. Because there is a **common difference** between consecutive terms, this is an example of an **arithmetic sequence**. An **arithmetic series** is the indicated sum of the terms in an arithmetic sequence. You cannot find the sum of all the terms in the sequence above because the numbers increase forever. However, you could find S_n, which is the sum of the first n terms in the sequence. This is sometimes called the nth partial sum.

EXAMPLE 1

For the arithmetic sequence shown above, find S_1, S_2, S_3, S_4, and S_5.

a. Write those partial sums as a sequence.

b. Graph the sequence. What type of function does the graph resemble?

STRATEGY   **Find the sequence of partial sums. Then graph them.**

STEP 1   Find the partial sums.

$S_1 = 2$

$S_2 = 2 + 4 = 6$

$S_3 = 2 + 4 + 6 = 12$

$S_4 = 2 + 4 + 6 + 8 = 20$

$S_5 = 2 + 4 + 6 + 8 + 10 = 30$

STEP 2   Represent the sequence of partial sums in a table.

n	1	2	3	4	5
S_n	2	6	12	20	30

STEP 3   Plot the points in the table on a coordinate grid.

The domain is only whole numbers from 1 to 5, so the points should not be connected. However, you can connect the points with a dashed line if it helps you see the shape of the graph better.

The curve looks like part of a parabola, so the graph looks like part of a quadratic equation.

SOLUTION   **a. The sequence of partial sums is: 2, 6, 12, 20, 30. b. The graph is shown under Step 3. It resembles the graph of a quadratic equation with a restricted domain.**

You could use this equation to find any partial sum for the sequence in Example 1:

$$S_n = n^2 + n$$

Since the variable n is raised to the second power, the sequence of partial sums is an example of a quadratic function.

> The formula for finding the nth partial sum of an arithmetic sequence is:
>
> $$S_n = \frac{n}{2}[a_1 + (a_1 + (n - 1)d)],$$
>
> where a_1 stands for the first term in the sequence and d is the common difference.

EXAMPLE 2

Is every sequence of partial sums of an arithmetic sequence an example of a quadratic function? Explain.

STRATEGY   **Expand the formula for finding any S_n. Decide if the equation is quadratic.**

STEP 1   Expand the formula.

$$S_n = \frac{n}{2}[a_1 + (a_1 + (n - 1)d)]$$

$$= \frac{n}{2}[a_1 + (a_1 + nd - d)]$$

$$= \frac{1}{2}(a_1 n + a_1 n + n^2 d - dn)$$

STEP 2   Is the equation above quadratic?

The equation above has a variable, n, raised to the second power. So, it is quadratic.

SOLUTION   **Any sequence of partial sums of an arithmetic sequence is an example of a quadratic function because n is always raised to the second power.**

A **finite arithmetic series** is an arithmetic series that contains both the first term and the final, or nth, term in the series. If you know both the first term (a_1) and the nth term (a_n), you can use a simpler formula to find the nth partial sum:

$$S_n = \frac{n}{2}(a_1 + a_n)$$

EXAMPLE 3

Find the 10th partial sum of this arithmetic sequence: 50, 35, 20, 5, −10, …

STRATEGY   **Use the formula.**

  STEP 1   Find the values you need.

  The common difference is: $d = 35 - 50 = -15$

  The first term is: $a_1 = 50$

  You are finding the 10th partial sum, so $n = 10$.

  STEP 2   Use the formula.

  $$S_n = \frac{n}{2}[a_1 + (a_1 + (n - 1)d)]$$

  $$S_{10} = \frac{10}{2}[50 + (50 + (10 - 1) \cdot -15)] = 5(50 + (-85)) = -175$$

SOLUTION   **The 10th partial sum is −175.**

Since an arithmetic series is a sum, it can be represented with summation notation, like this:

last value of k ⟶ 20

Greek letter sigma ⟶ $\sum_{k=1}$ $(5 + 2k)$ ⟵ formula for sequence

first value of k ⟶

k is called the index of summation, and it can be represented by any letter. The values of k begin with the integer after the equal sign and end with the number above the Greek letter *sigma*. In the example above, the values of k are the integers from 1 through 20.

COACHED EXAMPLE

Find the indicated sum for this arithmetic series: $\displaystyle\sum_{k=1}^{20} (5 + 2k)$

THINKING IT THROUGH

Find the first term. Substitute $k = 1$ into the given formula.

$a_1 = 5 + 2k = 5 + 2(\underline{\hspace{2cm}}) = \underline{\hspace{2cm}}$

Find the 20th term.

$a_{20} = 5 + 2(\underline{\hspace{2cm}}) = \underline{\hspace{2cm}}$

Find S_{20}.

$S_n = \frac{n}{2}(a_1 + a_n)$

$S_{20} = \underline{\hspace{8cm}}$

The 20th partial sum for the arithmetic series is $\underline{\hspace{3cm}}$**.**

Lesson Practice

Choose the correct answer.

1. For the arithmetic sequence shown below, find the first 5 partial sums.

   5, 13, 21, 29, 37, …

   Which shows the sequence of those partial sums?

   A. 5, 18, 21, 29, 37

   B. 5, 18, 26, 34, 42

   C. 5, 18, 39, 68, 105

   D. 5, 8, 5, 8, 5

2. For the arithmetic sequence shown below, find the first 5 partial sums.

   26, 14, 2, −10, −22, …

   Which shows the sequence of those partial sums?

   A. 26, 2, 4, −8, −30

   B. 26, 40, 42, 32, 10

   C. 26, 40, 16, −8, −32

   D. 26, 40, 42, 52, 74

3. Which is the 49th partial sum of this arithmetic sequence?

   1, 1.5, 2, 2.5, 3, …

   A. 13

   B. 25

   C. 612.5

   D. 637

4. Which is the 20th partial sum of this arithmetic sequence?

   85, 80, 75, 70, 65, …

   A. 375

   B. 750

   C. 950

   D. 1,500

5. What is the indicated sum for the arithmetic series?

   $$\sum_{k=1}^{18} (10 - 2k)$$

   A. 306

   B. −9

   C. −162

   D. −468

6. What is the sum of the first 50 positive odd integers?

   A. 2,500

   B. 2,450

   C. 1,275

   D. 50

7. For an arithmetic sequence, $a_2 = 14$ and $a_3 = 24$. What is the 100th partial sum of that sequence?

   $$a_1 = 4$$
   $$a_{100} = 994$$

   A. 499   C. 25,150

   B. 1,900   D. 49,900

18 Solving Quadratic Equations Graphically

MM2A4.a, MM2A4.c, MM2P1.c, MM2P1.d

A **quadratic equation** is an equation that can be written in the standard form $ax^2 + bx + c = 0$, where a, b, and c are real numbers and $a \neq 0$. A quadratic equation can also be expressed as: $f(x) = ax^2 + bx + c$. The only difference between these equations is that one is set equal to 0 and the other is set equal to $f(x)$. For a quadratic function, the values of x that make $f(x) = 0$ are the zeros of the function. You can find the zeros of a function by finding the x-intercepts of the graph of the function. You can use what you know about the graphs of quadratic functions to find the **roots**, or solutions, of a quadratic equation.

EXAMPLE 1

Solve $x^2 - 4x + 3 = 0$.

STRATEGY   Graph the function.

STEP 1   Make a table of values. Draw the graph.

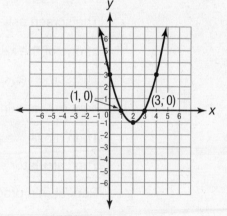

x	$f(x) = x^2 - 4x + 3$	$f(x)$
0	$f(0) = (0)^2 - 4(0) + 3 = 3$	3
1	$f(1) = (1)^2 - 4(1) + 3 = 0$	0
2	$f(2) = (2)^2 - 4(2) + 3 = -1$	−1
3	$f(3) = (3)^2 - 4(3) + 3 = 0$	0
4	$f(4) = (4)^2 - 4(4) + 3 = 3$	3

STEP 2   What values of x are solutions?

The x-intercepts are at (1, 0) and (3, 0), so the x-values that solve the equation are 1 and 3.

SOLUTION   The solutions, or roots, are $x = 1$ and $x = 3$.

If the solutions to a quadratic equation are not whole numbers, then it will be difficult to identify the zeros just by looking at a graph. But, you can still use graphing to find the solutions. Use a graphing calculator instead of paper and pencil. To review how to graph a function on your calculator, look back at Lesson 7, Example 3, on page 52.

EXAMPLE 2

Solve $-3x^2 + 5x = -12$.

STRATEGY   **Rewrite the equation in standard form. Then use a graphing calculator.**

STEP 1   Rewrite the equation in standard form.
$$-3x^2 + 5x = -12 \qquad \text{Add 12 to both sides.}$$
$$-3x^2 + 5x + 12 = 0$$

STEP 2   Graph the function on your calculator.
Enter: $Y_1 = -3X^2 + 5X + 12$. Then press GRAPH.

STEP 3   Find the zeros of the function.

Press 2nd TRACE .

This brings up the **CALCULATOR** menu. Press **2** to select **2:zero**.

The screen asks "Left bound?" Use the arrow keys to move the cursor to the left of one of the x-intercepts. Press ENTER.

The screen asks "Right bound?" Use the arrow keys to move the cursor to the right of that x-intercept. Press ENTER.

Then press ENTER again.

The calculator shows that one of the zeros is $-1.\overline{3}$, which is the same as $-\frac{4}{3}$.

Repeat this process to find the other zero for the function.

Zero
X=-1.333333   Y=0

Zero
X=3   Y=0

SOLUTION $x = -\frac{4}{3}$ and $x = 3$

Although in Examples 1 and 2 the quadratic equation had two real solutions, this is not true of all quadratic equations. A graph can help you identify the number of real solutions an equation has.

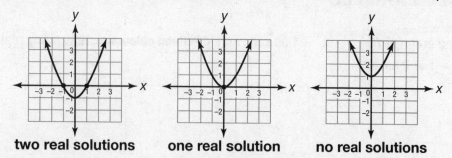

| **two real solutions** | **one real solution** | **no real solutions** |

The number of zeros a function has indicates the number of real solutions the quadratic equation has. The third graph above shows a function with no zeros, so it has no real solutions. It has complex solutions, but you cannot identify them by looking at a coordinate plane.

EXAMPLE 3

How many real solutions does $-x^2 - 2x - 1 = 0$ have? Identify the solutions, if any.

STRATEGY   **Use a graphing calculator. Observe the number of x-intercepts the graph shows.**

STEP 1   Graph the function on your calculator.

Enter: $Y_1 = -X^2 - 2X - 1$. Then press GRAPH .

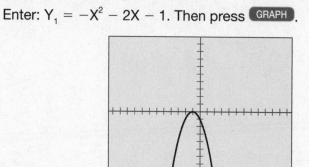

STEP 2   How many real solutions does the equation have?

The graph has only one x-intercept at $(-1, 0)$. So, its only zero is -1.

You can check this by using the **TABLE** or **CALCULATOR** functions on your calculator.

SOLUTION   **The equation has one real solution, $x = -1$.**

COACHED EXAMPLE

Below is the graph of $f(x) = -x^2 - 1$ as seen on a graphing calculator. How many real solutions does $-x^2 - 1 = 0$ have?

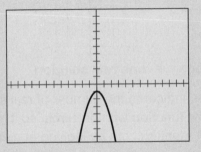

THINKING IT THROUGH

How many x-intercepts does the function have? _____

That means it has _____ zero(s) and _____ real solutions.

The function $f(x) = -x^2 - 1$ has _____ real solutions.

Lesson Practice

Choose the correct answer.

For questions 1 and 2, use your graphing calculator to check your answer.

1. Below is the graph of $f(x) = x^2 + 14x + 45$.

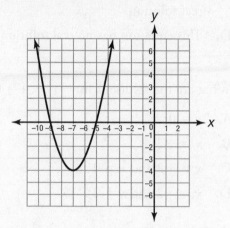

According to the graph, what are the solutions for $x^2 + 14x + 45 = 0$?

A. $x = -9$ and $x = -5$

B. $x = -9$ and $x = 0$

C. $x = -5$ and $x = 0$

D. $x = 0$ only

2. Below is the graph of $f(x) = \frac{1}{2}x^2 - 6x + 18$.

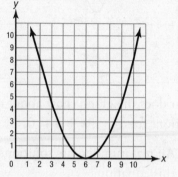

According to the graph, what are the solutions for $\frac{1}{2}x^2 - 6x + 18 = 0$?

A. $x = 4$ and $x = 8$

B. $x = 0$ and $x = 6$

C. $x = 6$ only

D. $x = 0$ only

3. Below is the graph of $f(x) = \frac{1}{4}x^2 + \frac{3}{2}x - \frac{1}{2}$.

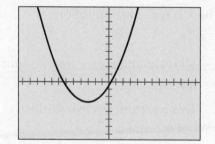

What does the graph show about the solutions for $\frac{1}{4}x^2 + \frac{3}{2}x - \frac{1}{2} = 0$?

A. All real numbers are solutions for this equation.

B. This equation has two distinct real solutions.

C. This equation has only one distinct real solution.

D. This equation has no real solutions.

4. Below is the graph of $f(x) = x^2 + 3x + 4$.

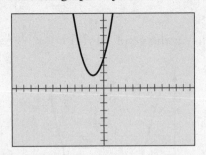

What does the graph show about the solutions for $x^2 + 3x + 4 = 0$?

A. All real numbers are solutions for this equation.

B. This equation has two distinct real solutions.

C. This equation has only one distinct real solution.

D. This equation has no real solutions.

Use your graphing calculator for questions 5–9.

5. Which is true of the solutions for $-7x + 3x^2 = 0$?

A. All real numbers are solutions for this equation.

B. This equation has two distinct real solutions.

C. This equation has only one distinct real solution.

D. This equation has no real solutions.

6. Which is true of the solutions for $2x^2 - 28x + 98 = 0$?

A. All real numbers are solutions for this equation.

B. This equation has two distinct real solutions.

C. This equation has only one distinct real solution.

D. This equation has no real solutions.

7. What are the solutions for $-x^2 + 4 = 0$?

A. $x = 0$

B. $x = -2$

C. $x = -2$ and $x = 0$

D. $x = -2$ and $x = 2$

8. What are the solutions for $5x^2 - 40x + 85 = 0$?

A. $x = -5$ and $x = -17$

B. $x = 5$ and $x = 17$

C. $x = 85$ only

D. There are no real solutions.

9. What are the solutions for $3x^2 - 14x - 24 = 0$?

A. $x = -\frac{4}{3}$ and $x = 6$

B. $x = -\frac{4}{3}$ and $x = 0$

C. $x = -6$ and $x = \frac{4}{3}$

D. $x = -6$ and $x = 0$

19 Solving Quadratic Equations Algebraically

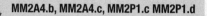
MM2A4.b, MM2A4.c, MM2P1.c MM2P1.d

There are several different ways to solve quadratic equations using algebra. One way is to factor the polynomial on one side of the equation into two **binomial** factors. Then, you can use the **zero product property** shown below to solve the equation.

> **Zero Product Property**
>
> If $ab = 0$, then $a = 0$ and/or $b = 0$.

After you factor the polynomial side, set each binomial factor equal to 0 and solve for x.

EXAMPLE 1

Solve this equation by factoring: $x^2 + 2x - 8 = 0$.

STRATEGY **Factor the left side of the equation. Set each binomial factor equal to 0 and solve for x.**

STEP 1   Factor the polynomial on the left side of the equation.

The factor pairs that give a product of -8 are: -1 and 8, 1 and -8, -2 and 4, and 4 and -2.

Try binomials that use these pairs. Then multiply to see if they work.

$(x - 1)(x + 8) = x^2 + 7x - 8$, so those factors do *not* work.

$(x + 1)(x - 8) = x^2 - 7x - 8$, so those factors do *not* work.

$(x - 2)(x + 4) = x^2 + 2x - 8$, so those factors *do* work.

There is no need to try any more factor pairs since you found a pair that work.

STEP 2   Set each factor equal to 0 and solve.

$(x - 2)(x + 4) = 0$, so:

$(x - 2) = 0$	$(x + 4) = 0$
$x = 2$	$x = -4$

SOLUTION   **The solutions are $x = 2$ and $x = -4$.**

Another way to solve quadratic equations is to take the square root of both sides.

Square Root Principle

If $u^2 = c$ and $c > 0$, then $u = \pm\sqrt{c}$.

EXAMPLE 2

Solve this equation using the square root principle: $x^2 - 2x + 1 = 12$.

STRATEGY   **Factor the polynomial side. Then take the square root of both sides.**

STEP 1   Factor the left side.

The factor pairs of 1 are: 1 and 1 and -1 and -1. Try binomials that use those numbers.

$(x + 1)(x + 1) = x^2 + 2x + 1$, so those factors do *not* work.

$(x - 1)(x - 1) = x^2 - 2x + 1$, so those factors *do* work.

Rewrite the equation using those factors: $(x - 1)^2 = 12$.

STEP 2   Take the square root of both sides of the equation.

$$\sqrt{(x - 1)^2} = \sqrt{12}$$
$$x - 1 = \pm\sqrt{12}$$

STEP 3   Add 1 to both sides to solve for x.

$x - 1 = \pm\sqrt{12}$, so $x = 1 + \sqrt{12} \approx 4.46$ *or* $x = 1 - \sqrt{12} \approx -2.46$

As shown above, you can use a calculator to approximate the values of x.

SOLUTION   **The solutions are $x = 1 + \sqrt{12}$ or $x = 1 - \sqrt{12}$.**

A third way to solve a quadratic equation is to use the **quadratic formula**. This formula is useful because it can be used to solve any quadratic equation, and is especially useful when an equation cannot be easily factored.

Quadratic Formula

If a quadratic equation is in the form $ax^2 + bx + c = 0$ and $a \neq 0$, then:

$$x = \frac{-b \pm \sqrt{b^2 - 4ac}}{2a}$$

EXAMPLE 3

Use the quadratic formula to find the roots of $3x^2 - 5x + 2 = 0$.

STRATEGY   **Use the quadratic formula to solve for *x*.**

STEP 1   Identify the values of *a*, *b*, and *c* in the equation.

In $3x^2 - 5x + 2 = 0$, $a = 3$, $b = -5$, and $c = 2$.

STEP 2   Substitute those values into the quadratic formula and solve.

$$x = \frac{-b \pm \sqrt{b^2 - 4ac}}{2a} = \frac{-(-5) \pm \sqrt{(-5)^2 - 4(3)(2)}}{(2)(3)}$$

$$= \frac{5 \pm \sqrt{25 - 24}}{6} = \frac{5 \pm \sqrt{1}}{6} = \frac{5}{6} \pm \frac{1}{6}, \text{ so:}$$

$$x = \frac{5}{6} + \frac{1}{6} = \frac{6}{6} = 1 \qquad x = \frac{5}{6} - \frac{1}{6} = \frac{4}{6} = \frac{2}{3}$$

SOLUTION   **The roots are $x = \frac{2}{3}$ and $x = 1$.**

In Lesson 18, you learned how you can use the graph of a quadratic function to determine how many real roots a quadratic equation has. Another way to determine this is to use the **discriminant**. The discriminant is the part of the quadratic formula shown below.

$$\frac{-b \pm \sqrt{\boxed{b^2 - 4ac}}}{2a} \longleftarrow \text{discriminant}$$

- If $b^2 - 4ac > 0$, the equation has 2 distinct real solutions.

- If $b^2 - 4ac = 0$, the equation has 1 real solution.

- If $b^2 - 4ac < 0$, the equation has no real solutions.

If an equation has no real solutions, you can use what you know about complex numbers to find its complex solutions.

EXAMPLE 4

Prove that the equation $x^2 - 2x = -10$ has no real solutions. Then find its complex solutions.

STRATEGY **Use the discriminant to show that the equation has no real solutions. Then use the quadratic equation to solve.**

STEP 1 Rewrite the equation in standard form, $ax^2 + bx + c = 0$.

$$x^2 - 2x + 10 = -10 + 10 \qquad \text{Add 10 to both sides.}$$
$$x^2 - 2x + 10 = 0$$

STEP 2 Find the discriminant.

In $x^2 - 2x + 10 = 0$, $a = 1$, $b = -2$, and $c = 10$.

The discriminant is $b^2 - 4ac = (-2)^2 - 4(1)(10) = 4 - 40 = -36$

STEP 3 Does the equation have any real solutions?

Since $b^2 - 4ac < 0$, the equation has no real solutions.

STEP 4 Use the quadratic formula to find the complex solutions.

$$x = \frac{-b \pm \sqrt{b^2 - 4ac}}{2a} = \frac{-(-2) \pm \sqrt{-36}}{(2)(1)} = \frac{2 \pm \sqrt{-36}}{2} = \frac{2 \pm 6i}{2} = 1 \pm 3i$$

SOLUTION **The discriminant is less than zero so the equation has no real solutions. Its complex solutions are $x = 1 + 3i$ and $x = 1 - 3i$.**

COACHED EXAMPLE

Use the quadratic formula to solve $x^2 + 8x = -4$.

THINKING IT THROUGH

Add _____ to both sides of the equation to convert the equation to standard form.

$x^2 + 8x + $ _____ $ = -4 + $ _____

$x^2 + 8x + $ _____ $ = 0$

In the equation above, $a = $ _____, $b = $ _____, and $c = $ _____.

Substitute those values into the quadratic formula and solve.

$$x = \frac{-b \pm \sqrt{b^2 - 4ac}}{2a}$$

$$= \frac{-(\underline{\quad}) \pm \sqrt{(\underline{\quad})^2 - (4)(\underline{\quad})(\underline{\quad})}}{(2)(\underline{\quad})} = \underline{\hspace{4cm}}$$

The solutions are $x = $ _____ and $x = $ _____.

Lesson Practice

Choose the correct answer.

1. Solve by factoring.

   $$x^2 - 2x - 15 = 0$$

   A. $x = 1$ and $x = 15$

   B. $x = -3$ and $x = 5$

   C. $x = -5$ and $x = 3$

   D. $x = -15$ and $x = 1$

2. Solve using the square root principle.

   $$x^2 + 14x + 49 = 5$$

   A. $x = -7 \pm \sqrt{5}$

   B. $x = \pm 2\sqrt{3}$

   C. $x = \pm 7\sqrt{5}$

   D. $x = 7 \pm \sqrt{5}$

3. Solve using the quadratic formula.

   $$x^2 - 8x + 2 = 0$$

   A. $x = 8 \pm 2\sqrt{14}$

   B. $x = 8 \pm \sqrt{14}$

   C. $x = 4 \pm 2\sqrt{14}$

   D. $x = 4 \pm \sqrt{14}$

4. Which is true of the solutions for $3x^2 - 7x = -10$?

   A. All real numbers are solutions.

   B. There are two real solutions.

   C. There is one real solution.

   D. There are complex solutions.

Solve the equations in questions 5–8.

5. $x^2 - 10x + 9 = 0$

   A. $x = -3$

   B. $x = 3$

   C. $x = 9$ and $x = 1$

   D. $x = -9$ and $x = -1$

6. $2x^2 + 4x - 3 = 0$

   A. $x = -4 \pm 2\sqrt{10}$

   B. $x = -4 \pm \dfrac{\sqrt{10}}{2}$

   C. $x = -1 \pm 2\sqrt{10}$

   D. $x = -1 \pm \dfrac{\sqrt{10}}{2}$

7. $2x^2 - 8x + 9 = 0$

   A. $x = 2 \pm \dfrac{i\sqrt{2}}{2}$

   B. $x = 2 \pm 2i\sqrt{2}$

   C. $x = 2 \pm 8i$

   D. $x = 4 \pm \dfrac{i\sqrt{2}}{2}$

8. $5x^2 = 30$

   A. $x = \pm\sqrt{6}$

   B. $x = \pm 3\sqrt{2}$

   C. $x = \pm 5$

   D. $x = \pm 6$

20 Solving Quadratic Inequalities

MM2A4.d, MM2P1.c, MM2P1.d

To solve a quadratic inequality using algebra, solve the inequality as if you were solving an equation. Then test values on the number line to determine which values are solutions.

EXAMPLE 1

Solve: $12 \leq 2x^2 - 5x$

STRATEGY   **Solve the inequality as if it were an equation. Then use a number line to test values of x and find the solution.**

STEP 1   Write the inequality in standard form.

$$12 - 12 \leq 2x^2 - 5x - 12 \qquad \text{Subtract 12 from both sides.}$$
$$0 \leq 2x^2 - 5x - 12$$

STEP 2   Replace the $\leq$ with an equal (=) sign.

$$0 = 2x^2 - 5x - 12$$

STEP 3   Use factoring and the **zero product property** to solve.

$$0 = (2x + 3)(x - 4), \text{ so:}$$

$2x + 3 = 0$	$x - 4 = 0$
$2x = -3$	$x = 4$
$x = -\dfrac{3}{2}$	

STEP 4   Plot those points on a number line and test values.

Since $-\dfrac{3}{2}$ and 4 are possible values of x, draw closed endpoints for those points.

This divides the number line into three sections. Test one number in each section.

Test: $x = -5$ | $x = 0$ | $x = 5$

$$
\begin{array}{l}
12 \stackrel{?}{\leq} 2(-5^2) - (-5) \\
12 \stackrel{?}{\leq} 2(25) + 5 \\
12 \leq 55 \checkmark \\
-5 \text{ is a solution.}
\end{array}
$$

$$
\begin{array}{l}
12 \stackrel{?}{\leq} 2(0)^2 - 0 \\
12 \stackrel{?}{\leq} 0 - 0 \\
12 \not\leq 0 \\
0 \text{ is } not \text{ a solution.}
\end{array}
$$

$$
\begin{array}{l}
12 \stackrel{?}{\leq} 2(5^2) - 5 \\
12 \stackrel{?}{\leq} 2(25) - 5 \\
12 \leq 45 \checkmark \\
5 \text{ is a solution.}
\end{array}
$$

STEP 5   Graph the solution.

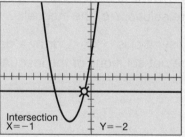

SOLUTION   The solution is $x \leq -\dfrac{3}{2}$ or $x \geq 4$.

You can also use graph paper or a graphing calculator to solve quadratic inequalities. If you need to review how to use a graphing calculator to perform some of the functions described in Example 2, look back at Lesson 7, Example 3, on page 52, and Lesson 8, Example 3, on page 58.

EXAMPLE 2

Solve: $x^2 + 6x + 3 \leq -2$

STRATEGY   **Graph the inequality using a graphing calculator.**

STEP 1   Enter the expression on the left side of the equation as Y_1.

Enter: $Y_1 = X^2 + 6X + 3$.

STEP 2   Enter the value on the right side of the equation as Y_2.

Enter: $Y_2 = -2$

STEP 3   Graph the functions on the calculator and find the points of intersection.

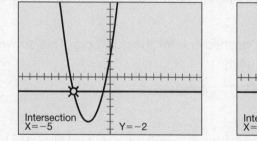

The graphs intersect when $x = -5$ and when $x = -1$.

STEP 4   Use the calculator to find the solution.

The original inequality was $x^2 + 6x + 3 \leq -2$.

You know that the inequality is true when x is *equal* to -5 and when x is *equal* to -1, because those are the points of intersection. Use the table below to find the x-values for which the y_1-values are less than or equal to the y_2-values.

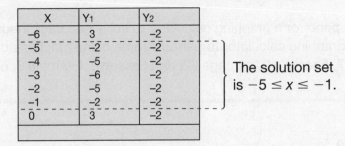

X	Y₁	Y₂
−6	3	−2
−5	−2	−2
−4	−5	−2
−3	−6	−2
−2	−5	−2
−1	−2	−2
0	3	−2

The solution set is $-5 \leq x \leq -1$.

Note: If you drew the graph on paper, you could test points that were less than -5, between -5 and -1, and greater than -1 to determine the solutions.

SOLUTION   **The solution set is $-5 \leq x \leq -1$.**

Examples 1 and 2 solved one-variable inequalities. The solutions were values of x. If you solve a two-variable inequality, the solutions will be ordered pairs in the form (x, y).

When graphing the parabola for a two-variable quadratic inequality:

- If the inequality symbol is $\geq$ or $\leq$, draw a solid line for the parabola. This shows that points on the parabola are solutions of the inequality.

- If the inequality symbol is $>$ or $<$, draw a dashed line for the parabola. This shows that points on the parabola are not solutions of the inequality.

EXAMPLE 3

Solve: $y < -x^2 - 2x + 2$

STRATEGY   **Write the inequality as an equation and graph it. Then determine the solutions of the original inequality.**

STEP 1   Rewrite the inequality as an equation.

$y = -x^2 - 2x + 2$

STEP 2   Make a table for $y = -x^2 - 2x + 2$.

x	$y = -x^2 - 2x + 2$	y
−4	$y = -(-4)^2 - 2(-4) + 2 = -6$	−6
−3	$y = -(-3)^2 - 2(-3) + 2 = -1$	−1
−2	$y = -(-2)^2 - 2(-2) + 2 = 2$	2
−1	$y = -(-1)^2 - 2(-1) + 2 = 3$	3
0	$y = -(0^2) - 2(0) + 2 = 2$	2
1	$y = -(1^2) - 2(1) + 2 = -1$	−1
2	$y = -(2^2) - 2(2) + 2 = -6$	−6

STEP 3   Use the table in Step 2 to graph the solutions.

The inequality symbol is $<$, so draw a dashed line for the parabola.

$y < -x^2 - 2x + 2$ means that the solution set is all *y*-values *less than* those on the parabola. Shade the region under the parabola.

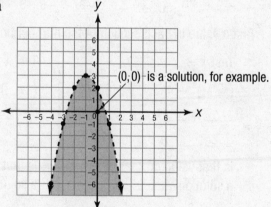

(0, 0) is a solution, for example.

STEP 4   Test a point to check that you shaded the correct region.

(0, 0) is in the shaded region. Test that (0, 0) solves the inequality.

$y < -x^2 - 2x + 2$

$0 \overset{?}{<} -(0)^2 - 2(0) + 2$

$0 \overset{?}{<} 0 - 0 + 2$

$0 < 2$ ✓

So, (0, 0) *is* a solution.

SOLUTION   **The graph in Step 3 shows all solutions for $y < -x^2 - 2x + 2$.**

COACHED EXAMPLE

Solve algebraically: $x^2 + 4x - 6 > 0$

THINKING IT THROUGH

Rewrite the inequality as an equation: _____

Use the quadratic formula to solve the equation.

$$x = \frac{-b \pm \sqrt{b^2 - 4ac}}{2a}$$

$$x = \frac{-\underline{\quad} \pm \sqrt{(\underline{\quad})^2 - (4)(\underline{\quad})(\underline{\quad})}}{(2)(\underline{\quad})}$$

$$= \underline{\hspace{8cm}}$$

Use your calculator to approximate the values of x.

$x \approx \underline{\hspace{2cm}}$ or $x \approx \underline{\hspace{2cm}}$

Plot those values of x on the number line below.

Use _____ endpoints because those values of x _____ solutions.

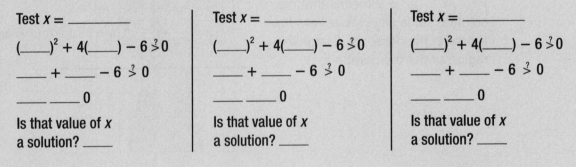

Test a value in each section of the number line.

Test $x =$ _____	Test $x =$ _____	Test $x =$ _____
$(\underline{\quad})^2 + 4(\underline{\quad}) - 6 \overset{?}{\gtrless} 0$	$(\underline{\quad})^2 + 4(\underline{\quad}) - 6 \overset{?}{\gtrless} 0$	$(\underline{\quad})^2 + 4(\underline{\quad}) - 6 \overset{?}{\gtrless} 0$
$\underline{\quad} + \underline{\quad} - 6 \overset{?}{\gtrless} 0$	$\underline{\quad} + \underline{\quad} - 6 \overset{?}{\gtrless} 0$	$\underline{\quad} + \underline{\quad} - 6 \overset{?}{\gtrless} 0$
$\underline{\quad}\ \underline{\quad}\ 0$	$\underline{\quad}\ \underline{\quad}\ 0$	$\underline{\quad}\ \underline{\quad}\ 0$
Is that value of x a solution? _____	Is that value of x a solution? _____	Is that value of x a solution? _____

Graph the entire solution on the number line above.

The approximate solution is _____.

Lesson Practice

Choose the correct answer.

1. What is the solution for $x^2 + 7x > -10$?

   A. $x < -5$ or $x > -2$

   B. $x < 2$ or $x > 5$

   C. $-2 < x < -5$

   D. $2 < x < 5$

2. Navi is solving $x^2 - 9x + 8 > -10$. He correctly entered this into his graphing calculator: $Y_1 = x^2 - 9x + 8$ and $Y_2 = -10$. He then looked at the table below.

X	Y₁	Y₂
1	0	−10
2	−6	−10
3	−10	−10
4	−12	−10
5	−12	−10
6	−10	−10
7	−6	−10

   Based on these results, what is the solution?

   A. $-6 < x < -3$

   B. $3 < x < 6$

   C. $x < -6$ or $x > -3$

   D. $x < 3$ or $x > 6$

3. Which graph shows the solution for $x^2 + x - 30 < 0$?

   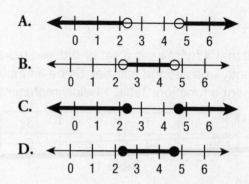

4. Which graph best shows the solution for $x^2 - 7x + 11 > 0$?

   A.
   B.
   C.
   D.

Solve the inequalities in questions 5 and 6.

5. $x^2 + 4x - 9 \le 0$

   A. $x \le 1.61$ or $x \ge 5.61$

   B. $x \le -5.61$ or $x \ge 1.61$

   C. $-1.61 \le x \le 5.61$

   D. $-5.61 \le x \le 1.61$

6. $x^2 + 3x + 2 \ge 0$

   A. $x \le -1$ or $x \ge 2$

   B. $x \le -2$ or $x \ge -1$

   C. $-2 \le x \le -1$

   D. $-1 \le x \le 2$

21 Functions and Their Inverses

MM2A5.b, MM2A5.c, MM2P5.a, MM2P5.b, MM2P5.c

Recall that a function is a set of ordered pairs in which each first number in the pair corresponds to exactly one second number. Since a function is a set of ordered pairs, a table can be used to represent a function. Table 1 below represents the function $f(x) = x + 3$, for the domain $\{1, 2, 3\}$.

x	1	2	3
y	4	5	6

Table 1

x	4	5	6
y	1	2	3

Table 2

In table 2 shown above, the first and second coordinates of the ordered pairs from the first table have been switched. Table 2 represents the **inverse** of $f(x) = x + 3$. This inverse function can be represented as: $f^{-1}(x) = x - 3$, for the domain $\{4, 5, 6\}$.

Notice that the domain of f is equal to the range of f^{-1} above, and vice versa. The notation $\boldsymbol{f^{-1}}$ indicates that it is an inverse function. Read the notation as "f inverse." Be careful: the notation *does not mean* it is a reciprocal.

A function and its inverse undo each other. One way to find the inverse of a function is to use the opposite of the order of operations to undo the operations.

EXAMPLE 1

Consider the linear function $f(x) = \frac{x}{4} - 2$.

a. Find its inverse.

b. Graph $y = x$ as a dashed line on a coordinate grid. On the same grid, graph $f(x)$ and its inverse $f^{-1}(x)$.

STRATEGY   Use inverse operations.

STEP 1   Describe the operations performed on x.

The function $f(x)$ divides each input value by 4 and then subtracts 2 from the quotient.

STEP 2   Describe how to undo those operations. Then write the inverse.

The inverse must add 2 to each input value and then multiply the sum by 4.

$f^{-1}(x) = 4(x + 2)$

STEP 3   Make tables to help you graph the function and its inverse.

Remember to use the range of $f(x)$ as the domain of $f^{-1}(x)$.

$f(x) = \frac{x}{4} - 2$

x	y
−4	−3
0	−2
4	−1

$y = 4(x + 2)$

x	y
−3	−4
−2	0
−1	4

STEP 4   Graph $y = x$, $f(x)$, and its inverse.

Graph $y = x$ as a dashed line through (0, 0), and (1, 1).

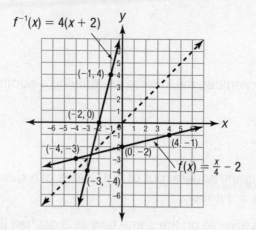

Notice that $(-4, -3)$ and $(-3, -4)$ are the same distance from the line $y = x$. The same is true of $(0, -2)$ and $(-2, 0)$ and of $(4, -1)$ and $(-1, 4)$. Each point on the inverse is a reflection across $y = x$ of a point on the original function.

SOLUTION   **The inverse of $f(x) = \frac{x}{4} - 2$ is $f^{-1}(x) = 4(x + 2)$. The graphs of the function and its inverse are shown in Step 4.**

Another way to find the inverse of a function is to replace $f(x)$ with y and then reverse x and y in the equation. Solve the new equation for y to find the inverse.

EXAMPLE 2

Find the inverse of $f(x) = x^2$. Then graph the function and its inverse. (**Note:** You cannot use the notation $f^{-1}(x)$ for the inverse because the inverse is not a function.)

STRATEGY   Reverse x and y. Then graph $f(x) = x^2$ and its inverse.

STEP 1   Replace $f(x)$ with y. Then reverse x and y.

$$f(x) = x^2$$
$$y = x^2$$
$$x = y^2$$

STEP 2   Solve for y. Remember, the inverse of squaring a number is taking its square root.

$$x = y^2$$
$$\sqrt{x} = \sqrt{y^2}$$
$$\pm\sqrt{x} = y$$

When taking the square root of both sides of a quadratic equation, remember to include the $\pm$ symbol.

STEP 3   Graph f and its inverse on the same grid as a dashed line showing $y = x$.

Make tables to help you draw the graphs.

$f(x) = x^2$

x	y
−2	4
−1	1
0	0
1	1
2	4

$y = +\sqrt{x}$

x	y
0	0
1	1
4	2

$y = -\sqrt{x}$

x	y
0	0 → already included
1	−1
4	−2

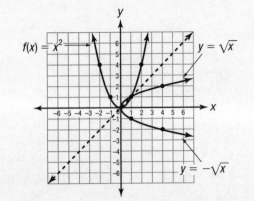

SOLUTION   The graph of $f(x) = x^2$ and its inverse, $y = \pm\sqrt{x}$, are shown in Step 3.

The graphs in Examples 1 and 2 show that each point on the graph of a function is reflected across $y = x$ to form a point on its inverse. Use that information to help you understand what happens when you find the inverse of $f(x) = \frac{5}{x}$.

EXAMPLE 3

The graph of $f(x) = \frac{5}{x}$ is shown below. The dashed line shows $y = x$. Find its inverse. What do you notice about the function and its inverse?

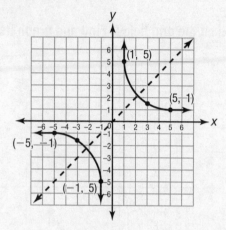

STRATEGY   **Reverse *x* and *y*. Then graph *f*(x) and its inverse.**

STEP 1   Replace $f(x)$ with y. Then reverse x and y.

$$f(x) = \frac{5}{x}$$

$$y = \frac{5}{x}$$

$$x = \frac{5}{y}$$

STEP 2   Solve for y.

$$x = \frac{5}{y}$$

$$xy = 5$$

$$y = \frac{5}{x}$$

STEP 3   What do you notice about the original function and its inverse?

The original function is $f(x) = \frac{5}{x}$ or $y = \frac{5}{x}$. The inverse has the same equation, $y = \frac{5}{x}$.

If you graph $f(x)$ and its inverse, both graphs will have the same points. This means that $f(x) = \frac{5}{x}$ is its own inverse.

Look at the graph. Notice that $(1, 5)$ is the reflection of $(5, 1)$ across $y = x$. The graph is symmetrical with respect to $y = x$, just as a function and its inverse are symmetrical with respect to that line. That can help you recognize when a function is its own inverse.

SOLUTION   **The function $f(x) = \frac{5}{x}$ is its own inverse.**

A **power function** is a function in the form $f(x) = x^a$, where a is a real number and $a \neq 0$. You may think, at first, that a power function looks similar to an exponential function, which is written in the form $f(x) = a^x$. However, they are not the same. In a power function, the base is a variable and the exponent is a constant, whereas in an exponential function, the exponent is a variable and the base is a constant.

COACHED EXAMPLE

The graph of $f(x) = 8x^3$ is shown on the grid below. Find and graph its inverse.

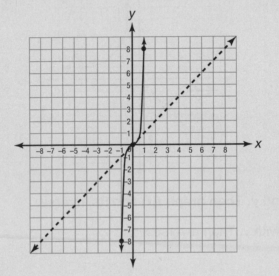

THINKING IT THROUGH

Replace $f(x)$ with y. Then reverse x and y.

$$f(x) = 8x^3 \longrightarrow \underline{\hspace{1cm}} = 8x^3 \longrightarrow \underline{\hspace{1cm}} = \underline{\hspace{1.5cm}}$$

Solve for y. Remember, taking the cube root of a number is the inverse of raising a number to the power of 3.

_____

Fill in the table of values below for the inverse. Then, graph the inverse above.

x	y
−8	
0	
8	

The inverse of $f(x) = 8x^3$ is _____. The graph is shown above.

Lesson Practice

Choose the correct answer.

1. The graph of $f(x) = -2x + 3$ is shown on the grid below.

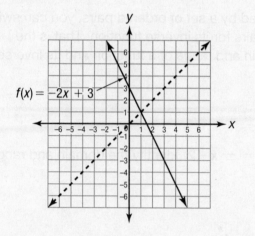

$f(x) = -2x + 3$

Which is **not** a point on the inverse of this function?

A. $(-5, 4)$ C. $(-1, 2)$

B. $(0, -3)$ D. $(5, -1)$

2. Which of the following is the inverse of $f(x) = 7x$?

A. $f^{-1}(x) = x + 7$

B. $f^{-1}(x) = x - 7$

C. $f^{-1}(x) = \frac{7}{x}$

D. $f^{-1}(x) = \frac{x}{7}$

3. Which of the following is the inverse of $f(x) = 4x^2$?

A. $y = \pm \frac{\sqrt{x}}{2}$

B. $y = \pm \sqrt{2x}$

C. $y = \pm 2x$

D. $y = \pm \frac{x}{2}$

4. The graph of $f(x) = x^3$ is shown on the grid below.

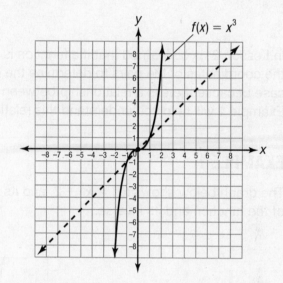

$f(x) = x^3$

Which is **not** a point on the inverse of this function?

A. $(-8, -2)$

B. $(-1, 1)$

C. $(0, 0)$

D. $(8, 2)$

5. Which of the following is the inverse of $f(x) = \frac{1}{4}x - 6$?

A. $f^{-1}(x) = \frac{(x + 6)}{4}$

B. $f^{-1}(x) = \frac{(x - 6)}{4}$

C. $f^{-1}(x) = 4(x + 6)$

D. $f^{-1}(x) = 4(x - 6)$

22 Characteristics of Functions and Their Inverses

MM2A5.a, MM2A5.c, MM2P3.a, MM2P3.b, MM2P4.b

In Lesson 21, you learned that if a function is represented by a set of ordered pairs, you can switch the coordinates of the pairs to determine the ordered pairs for its inverse function. That is the case because there is a relationship between the domain and range of a function and its inverse. Example 1 will help you understand this relationship.

EXAMPLE 1

The graph below shows $f(x) = x^2 + 2$, and its inverse, $y = \pm\sqrt{x - 2}$. Identify the domain and range of the function and its inverse.

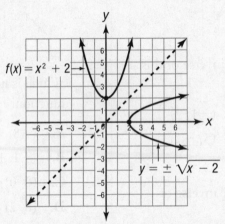

STRATEGY   **Find the domain and the range of the function and its inverse.**

STEP 1   Identify the domain and range of the original function, $f(x) = x^2 + 2$.

The arrows show that the possible values of x stretch from $-\infty$ to ∞, so the domain is the set of all real numbers.

The minimum value of the function is 2, so the range is all real numbers greater than or equal to 2, or $y \geq 2$.

STEP 2   Identify the domain and range of the inverse, $y = \pm\sqrt{x - 2}$.

The least x-value is 2, so the domain is all real numbers greater than or equal to 2, or $x \geq 2$.

The arrows show that the possible values of y stretch from $-\infty$ to ∞, so the range is the set of all real numbers.

STEP 3   What do you notice about the domains and ranges?

> The numbers that make up the domain of the inverse are the same numbers that make up the range of the original function: all real numbers greater than or equal to 2.

> The numbers that make up the range of the inverse are the same numbers that make up the domain of the original function: all real numbers.

SOLUTION   **The domain of $f(x) = x^2 + 2$ is the set of all real numbers. The range of its inverse is also the set of all real numbers. The range of $f(x) = x^2 + 2$ is $y \geq 2$. The domain of its inverse is $x \geq 2$.**

Sometimes, the domain of a function is restricted.

EXAMPLE 2

The graph below shows the same function as in Example 1, but with a restricted domain. Identify the domain and range of the function and its inverse.

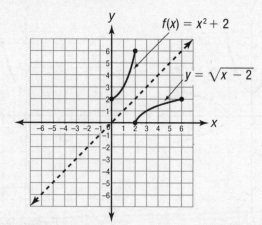

STEP 1   Identify the domain and range of the original function.

> The least x-value is 0. The greatest x-value is 2.

> The domain is $0 \leq x \leq 2$.

> The least y-value is 2. The greatest y-value is 6.

> The range is $2 \leq y \leq 6$.

STEP 2   Identify the domain and range of the inverse.

> Reverse the domain and the range of the original function.

> The domain is: $2 \leq x \leq 6$.

> The range is: $0 \leq y \leq 2$.

SOLUTION   **The domain of the function and the range of its inverse include all real numbers ≥ 0 and ≤ 2. The domain of the inverse and the range of the function include all real numbers ≥ 2 and ≤ 6.**

A **one-to-one function** is a function in which each *y*-value is paired with exactly one *x*-value. A one-to-one function has an inverse that is also a function. Except for horizontal lines, all linear functions are one-to-one functions. A function that is not one-to-one has an inverse that is not a function.

You can determine if a function is one-to-one using the **horizontal line test**. If a horizontal line can be drawn through the function that would pass through more than one point, then the function is not one-to-one and its inverse is not a function.

EXAMPLE 3

Look back at the two original functions in Examples 1 and 2. Use the Horizontal Line Test to determine which function has an inverse that is a function and which has an inverse that is not a function.

STRATEGY   **Apply the horizontal line test.**

STEP 1   Apply the horizontal line test to the original function in each graph.

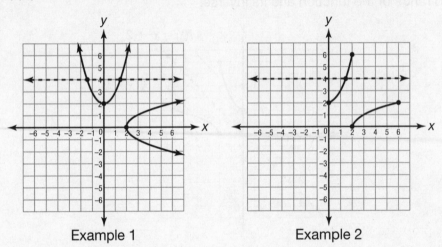

Example 1   Example 2

STEP 2   What does the test show?

The horizontal line drawn through the original function in Example 1 intersects the graph at more than one point. The function is not one-to-one and its inverse is not a function.

No horizontal line can be drawn through the original function in Example 2 that intersects the graph at more than one point. The function is one-to-one and its inverse is a function.

SOLUTION   **The original function in Example 1 is not one-to-one, so its inverse is not a function. The original function in Example 2 is one-to-one, so its inverse is a function.**

COACHED EXAMPLE

Is the inverse of $f(x) = -3x^5$ a function?

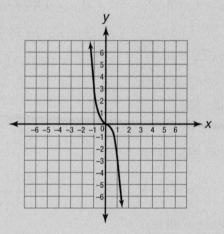

THINKING IT THROUGH

Use the horizontal line test.

If every horizontal line that can be drawn through the function passes through only _____ point(s), the function is a one-to-one function and its inverse is a function.

Draw one or more horizontal lines through the function above.

Is it possible to draw a horizontal line through the function that passes through more than one point? _____

Since you _____ draw a horizontal line that passes through two or more points, the function _____ a one-to-one function and its inverse _____ a function.

Lesson Practice

Choose the correct answer.

1. The domain of a function is $x \geq 0$. Which of the following must also be true?

   A. The function has a range of $y \geq 0$.

   B. The function is a one-to-one function.

   C. The inverse of the function has a domain of $x \geq 0$.

   D. The inverse of the function has a range of $y \geq 0$.

2. The range of a function is the set of all real numbers. Which of the following must also be true?

   A. The domain of the function is the set of all real numbers.

   B. The function is a one-to-one function.

   C. The domain of the inverse of the function is the set of all real numbers.

   D. The range of the inverse of the function is the set of all real numbers.

3. The range of a function is $y \geq 2$. Which of the following must also be true?

   A. The function has a domain of $x \geq 0$.

   B. The inverse of the function has a domain of $x \geq 2$.

   C. The inverse of the function has a range of $y \geq 2$.

   D. The function is not a one-to-one function.

Use this graph for questions 4 and 5.

The graph of $f(x) = \frac{1}{2x} - 1$ has a restricted domain. Its inverse $f^{-1}(x)$ and the dashed line $y = x$ are also graphed below.

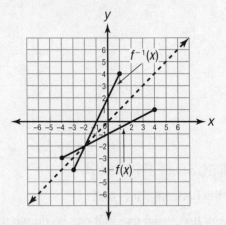

4. Which best describes the restricted domain of the original function $f(x) = \frac{1}{2}x - 1$?

   A. $-4 \leq x \leq 4$

   B. $-3 \leq x \leq 1$

   C. $x \geq -4$

   D. $x \geq -3$

5. Which best describes the range of the inverse of $f(x) = \frac{1}{2}x - 1$?

   A. $-4 \leq y \leq 4$

   B. $-3 \leq y \leq 1$

   C. $y \geq -4$

   D. $y \geq -3$

6. Which of the functions graphed below is **not** a one-to-one function?

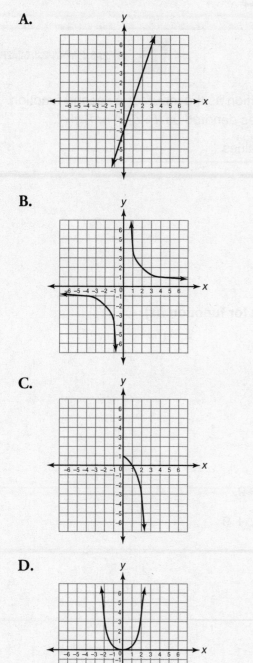

A.

B.

C.

D.

Use this graph for questions 7 and 8.

Below is the graph of $f(x) = 5x^3 - 1$, with a restricted domain.

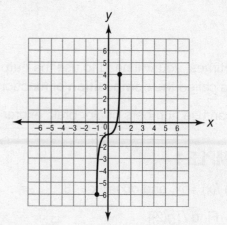

7. Which best describes the domain of the function?

   A. $-3 \leq x \leq 1$

   B. $-1 \leq x \leq 1$

   C. the set of all real numbers

   D. the set of all integers

8. Which is true of the inverse of the function?

   A. The inverse has a domain that includes all values of x greater than or equal to 0.

   B. The inverse has a range that includes all values of y greater than or equal to 0.

   C. The inverse is a function.

   D. The inverse is not a function.

23 Using Composition to Verify Inverse Functions

 MM2A5.d, MM2P2.d, MM2P3.c

Sometimes, you will need to use the output from one function as the input for a second function. This is called the **composition** of functions. It is sometimes denoted as $(f \circ g)(x)$ or $f[g(x)]$.

You can use numbers or algebraic expressions as input values.

EXAMPLE 1

Given $f(x) = x^2$ and $g(x) = x + 3$.

   a. Find $f[g(2)]$.

   b. Find $f[g(x)]$.

STRATEGY   **First find $g(2)$. Then use that as the input for function $f(x)$.**

  STEP 1   Find $g(2)$.

                $g(x) = x + 3$, so $g(2) = 2 + 3 = 5$.

  STEP 2   Now use that as the input for $f(x)$.

                $f(x) = x^2$, so $f[g(2)] = f(5) = 5^2 = 25$.

  STEP 3   Now find $f[g(x)]$.

                Use $x + 3$ as the input.

                $f[g(x)] = f(x + 3) = (x + 3)^2 = x^2 + 6x + 9$.

SOLUTION   a. $f[g(2)] = 25$ b. $f[g(x)] = x^2 + 6x + 9$

You can use composition to verify that two functions are inverses. When you compose a function and its inverse, the resulting output will be the same as the input value, x. This is true because a function and its inverse undo each other.

EXAMPLE 2

Use composition to verify that $f^{-1}(x) = \frac{x}{2} + 5$ is the inverse of $f(x) = 2x - 10$.

STRATEGY   **Find $f[f^{-1}(x)]$. Then find $f^{-1}[f(x)]$. If the resulting outputs are equal to x, then f^{-1} is the inverse of f.**

STEP 1   Find $f[f^{-1}(x)]$.

Use $\frac{x}{2} + 5$ as the input.

$f[f^{-1}(x)] = f\left(\frac{x}{2} + 5\right) = 2\left(\frac{x}{2} + 5\right) - 10 = \frac{2x}{2} + 10 - 10 = x$

That output is x. However, you must verify that both $f[f^{-1}(x)]$ and $f^{-1}[f(x)]$ give that output.

STEP 2   Find $f^{-1}[f(x)]$.

Use $2x - 10$ as the input.

$f^{-1}[f(x)] = f(2x - 10) = \frac{2x - 10}{2} + 5 = x - 5 + 5 = x$

Since both $f[f^{-1}(x)]$ and $f^{-1}[f(x)]$ result in x, the two functions are inverses.

SOLUTION   **The function $f^{-1}(x) = \frac{x}{2} + 5$ is the inverse of $f(x) = 2x - 10$ because $f[f^{-1}(x)] = f^{-1}[f(x)] = x$.**

EXAMPLE 3

For $x \geq 0$, $f(x) = \frac{1}{4}x^2$ and $g(x) = 4\sqrt{x}$. Use composition to determine if the two functions are inverses.

STRATEGY   **Determine if the outputs of both $f[g(x)]$ and $g[f(x)]$ are x.**

STEP 1   Find $f[g(x)]$.

Use $4\sqrt{x}$ as the input.

$f[g(x)] = f(4\sqrt{x}) = \frac{1}{4}(4\sqrt{x})^2 = \left(\frac{1}{4}\right)(16x) = 4x$

STEP 2   Do you need to find $g[f(x)]$?

No, you do not need to find $g[f(x)]$.

Since $f[g(x)] \neq x$, you know that the functions are not inverses.

SOLUTION   **$f[g(x)] = 4x$ not x, so the functions are not inverses.**

COACHED EXAMPLE

The inverse of $f(x) = \frac{6}{x}$ is $f^{-1}(x) = \frac{6}{x}$. Use composition to prove that $f(x) = \frac{6}{x}$ is its own inverse.

THINKING IT THROUGH

Find $f[f^{-1}(x)]$.

$f[f^{-1}(x)] = f\left(\frac{6}{x}\right) = $ _____

Was the output x? _____

Do you need to compute $f^{-1}[f(x)]$ to prove that the two functions are inverses? Explain.

_____

_____

_____

I can prove that $f(x) = \frac{6}{x}$ is its own inverse because $f[f^{-1}](x) = $ _____ and $f^{-1}[f(x)]$

_____.

Lesson Practice

Choose the correct answer.

1. Given $f(x) = x^2 + 1$ and $g(x) = \frac{1}{x}$. What is the value of $f\left[g\left(\frac{1}{2}\right)\right]$?

   A. $\frac{4}{5}$

   B. $\frac{5}{4}$

   C. 2

   D. 5

2. Given $f(x) = -x^2 - 2$ and $g(x) = 4x - 1$. What is the value of $g[f(-2)]$?

   A. 7

   B. −9

   C. −25

   D. −83

3. Two functions, $f(x)$ and $g(x)$, must be inverses of one another, if which of the following is true?

   A. either $f[g(x)] = x$ or $g[f(x)] = x$

   B. if $f[g(x)] = x$, but $g[f(x)] \neq x$

   C. if $g[g(x)] = x$, but $f[f(x)] \neq x$

   D. both $f[g(x)] = x$ and $g[f(x)] = x$

4. Given $f(x) = \frac{x}{3}$ and $g(x) = 6x + 9$. What is the value of $f[g(x)]$?

   A. x

   B. $2x + 3$

   C. $2x + 9$

   D. $6x + 9$

5. Given $f(x) = x^5$ and $g(x) = 2x$. What is the value of $f[g(x)]$?

   A. $2x^5$

   B. $10x^5$

   C. $32x^5$

   D. $2x^6$

6. Which pair of functions are inverses? Use composition to determine the answer.

   A. $f(x) = 3x + 2$ and $g(x) = 3x - 2$

   B. $f(x) = 3x + 2$ and $g(x) = \frac{x - 2}{3}$

   C. $f(x) = 3x$ and $g(x) = \frac{3}{x}$

   D. $f(x) = 3x$ and $g(x) = x - 3$

7. For $x \geq 4$, $f(x) = x^2 + 4$ and $g(x) = \sqrt{x - 4}$. Are the two functions inverses? Why or why not?

   A. Yes, because $f[g(x)] = x$ and $g[f(x)] = x$.

   B. Yes, because $f[g(x)] = x$ and $g[f(x)] = 1$.

   C. No, because even though $f[g(x)] = 1$, $g[f(x)] = x$.

   D. No, because $f[g(x)] = x$ and $g[f(x)] = x$.

1. Which shows $f(x) = -\frac{1}{3}x^2 - 4x - 22$ in vertex form?

    A. $f(x) = -\left(\frac{1}{3x} - 5^2\right) - 10$

    B. $f(x) = -\left(\frac{1}{3x} + 5^2\right) - 10$

    C. $f(x) = -\frac{1}{3}(x - 6)^2 - 10$

    D. $f(x) = -\frac{1}{3}(x + 6)^2 - 10$

2. Which shows the solutions of $x^2 - 20x + 100 = 32$?

    A. $x = 10 \pm 4\sqrt{2}$

    B. $x = 10 \pm 8\sqrt{2}$

    C. $x = 20 \pm 4\sqrt{2}$

    D. $x = 22$ and $x = 42$

3. Which of the following is the inverse of $f(x) = -\frac{1}{27}x^3$?

    A. $f^{-1}(x) = -3\sqrt[3]{x}$

    B. $f^{-1}(x) = -\frac{1}{3}\sqrt[3]{x}$

    C. $f^{-1}(x) = 3\sqrt[3]{x}$

    D. The function is its own inverse.

4. Which is true of the solutions for $9x^2 - 12x + 4 = 0$?

    A. All real numbers are solutions for this equation.

    B. This equation has two distinct real solutions.

    C. This equation has only one distinct real solution.

    D. This equation has no real solutions, but it does have complex solutions.

5. Below is the graph of $f(x) = -x^2 + 2x + 4$.

    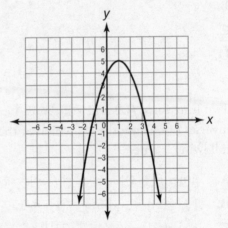

    Which of the following statements is NOT true?

    A. The function has two x-intercepts.

    B. The y-intercept of the function is at $(0, 4)$.

    C. The domain of the function is all real numbers ≤ 5.

    D. The function is increasing on the interval $\{-\infty < x < 1\}$.

6. Which graph best represents the first five partial sums for the arithmetic sequence below?

$$18, 14, 10, 6, 2, \dots$$

A.

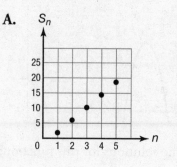

B.

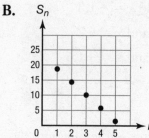

C.

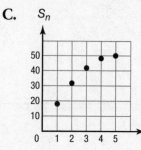

D.

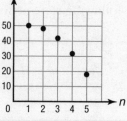

7. Which describes how the graph of $f(x) = x^2$ was transformed to form the graph of $h(x) = \left(\frac{1}{3}x\right)^2$?

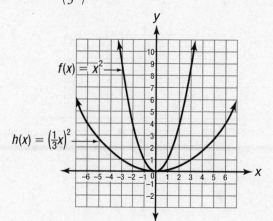

A. reflection across the x-axis

B. reflection across the y-axis

C. horizontal stretch of $f(x)$ by a factor of 3

D. vertical shrink of $f(x)$ by a factor of $\frac{1}{3}$

8. What is the solution of $x^2 - 13x \geq 19$?

A. $-14.33 \leq x \leq 1.33$

B. $-11.32 \leq x \leq 1.68$

C. $x \leq -1.33$ or $x \geq 14.33$

D. $x \leq 1.68$ or $x \geq 11.32$

9. Below is the graph of $f(x) = \frac{1}{2}x^2 - 3$, with a restricted domain. The dashed line on the grid shows $y = x$.

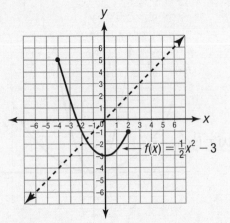

Which is NOT true of $f(x) = \frac{1}{2}x^2 - 3$ or its inverse?

A. The domain of its inverse is $-3 \leq x \leq 5$.

B. The range of its inverse is $-4 \leq y \leq 2$.

C. Its inverse is a function.

D. The function $f(x) = \frac{1}{2}x^2 - 3$ is not a one-to-one function.

10. Which is the 35th partial sum of this arithmetic sequence?

$$3, 4.5, 6, 7.5, 9, \ldots$$

A. 54

B. 210

C. 945

D. 997.5

11. The sketch below shows how the graph of $f(x) = -x^2 - \frac{15}{2}x - 11$ looks on a graphing calculator.

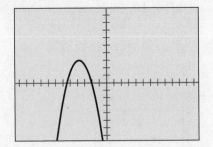

What are the solutions for this function?

A. $x = -6$ and $x = -1.5$

B. $x = -5.5$ and $x = -2$

C. $x = -5.5$ and $x = -1.5$

D. $x = 2$ and $x = 5.5$

12. What is the vertex of the function $f(x) = 5x^2 - 10x + 1$?

A. $(1, 4)$

B. $(1, -4)$

C. $(0, 1)$

D. $(-1, -4)$

13. For $x \geq 0$, $f(x) = 4x^2$ and $g(x) = \frac{\sqrt{x}}{2}$. Are the two functions inverses? Why or why not?

   A. Yes, because $f[g(x)] = x$ and $g[f(x)] = x$.

   B. Yes, because $f[g(x)] = 2x$ and $g[f(x)] = \frac{x}{2}$.

   C. No, because even though $f[g(x)] = x$, $g[f(x)] = \frac{x}{2}$.

   D. No, because $f[g(x)] = 2x$.

14. What are the solutions of $2x^2 - 8x + 10 = 0$?

   A. $x = \pm 4i$

   B. $x = 1 + 4i$ and $x = 2 - 4i$

   C. $x = 2 \pm i$

   D. $x = 2 + 4i$ and $x = 4 - 4i$

15. The dashed line on each grid below shows $y = x$. Which also shows the graph of $f(x) = 2x - 4$ and its inverse, $f^{-1}(x)$?

A.

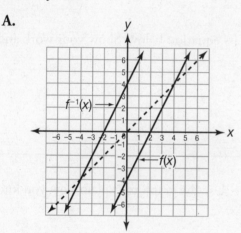

C.

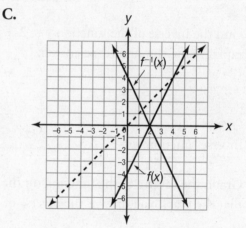

B.

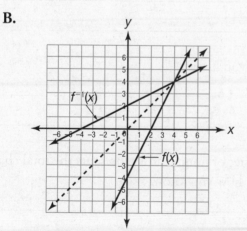

D.

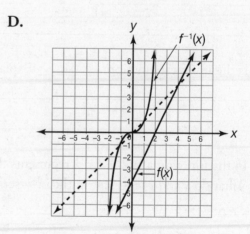

OPEN-ENDED QUESTION

16. For each babysitting job, Keisha charges $2 for bus fare plus $6 per hour for babysitting. So, the total amount she charges, y, for a job that lasts x hours is: $y = 2 + 6x$.

The graph below shows this function.

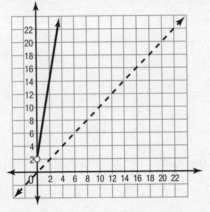

A. Find the inverse of the function $y = 2 + 6x$. Write its equation below. Show your work and/or explain how you found the answer.

Inverse function: $y =$ _____

B. Graph the inverse of the function on the grid above. Use the graph to explain how you know that the graph you drew is the inverse of $y = 2 + 6x$.

_____

_____

C. Is the inverse a function? _____ Explain how you know.

_____

_____

D. In the function $y = 2 + 6x$, x represents the number of hours and y represents the total charge. What do x and y represent in the inverse? Explain how you know.

x represents _____

_____

y represents _____

_____

17. The function $f(x) = x^2$ is graphed on the grid below

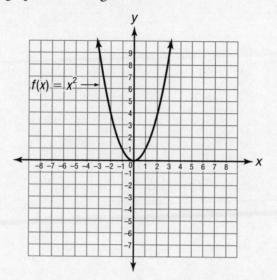

A. The function $h(x) = (x - 3)^2 - 2$ is the result of a transformation of $f(x) = x^2$. Graph $h(x)$ on the grid above. Then describe the two transformations needed to move $f(x) = x^2$ so that it completely covers $h(x) = (x - 3)^2 - 2$.

Transformations: _____

_____

B. The equation for $h(x) = (x - 3)^2 - 2$ is written in vertex form. How can you use that equation to determine the maximum or minimum, the vertex, and the axis of symmetry of the function? Label each on the grid above.

_____

_____

C. Convert the equation $h(x) = (x - 3)^2 - 2$ to standard form. Show your work.

Standard form: _____

CHAPTER
4 Geometry

24 Special Right Triangles

MM2G1.a, MM2G1.b

A **right triangle** is a triangle with one right angle. Sometimes, you may need to find the length of a side of a right triangle.

Knowing the angle measures of a right triangle can help you find a missing length for one of the special right triangles described below.

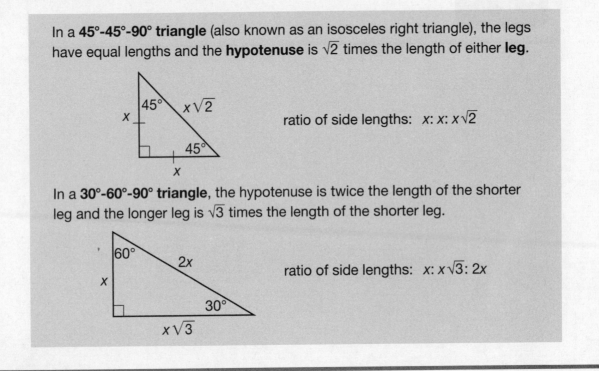

In a **45°-45°-90° triangle** (also known as an isosceles right triangle), the legs have equal lengths and the **hypotenuse** is $\sqrt{2}$ times the length of either **leg**.

ratio of side lengths: $x : x : x\sqrt{2}$

In a **30°-60°-90° triangle**, the hypotenuse is twice the length of the shorter leg and the longer leg is $\sqrt{3}$ times the length of the shorter leg.

ratio of side lengths: $x : x\sqrt{3} : 2x$

EXAMPLE 1

Find the missing lengths in the triangle shown below.

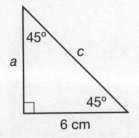

STRATEGY   Use what you know about 45°-45°-90° triangles.

STEP 1   Use what you know about the legs.

One leg in the triangle has an unknown length, a.

The other leg measures 6 centimeters.

The legs in a 45°-45°-90° triangle have equal lengths.

$a = 6$ cm

STEP 2   Use what you know about the relationship between a leg and the hypotenuse.

The hypotenuse has an unknown length, c.

The hypotenuse in a 45°-45°-90° triangle is $\sqrt{2}$ times the length of either leg.

$c = \sqrt{2} \cdot 6 = 6\sqrt{2}$ cm

SOLUTION   In the triangle above, $a = 6$ centimeters and $c = 6\sqrt{2}$ centimeters.

EXAMPLE 2

Find the missing lengths in the triangle.

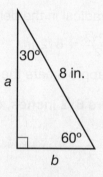

STRATEGY   Use what you know about 30°-60°-90° triangles.

STEP 1   Find the length of the shorter leg.

The shorter leg measures b inches. The hypotenuse measures 8 inches.

The hypotenuse in a 30°-60°-90° triangle is twice the length of the shorter leg, so:

$2b = 8$

$b = 4$ in.

STEP 2   Use the length you found for the shorter leg to find the length of the longer leg.

The longer leg is $\sqrt{3}$ times the length of the shorter leg.

$a = \sqrt{3} \cdot b = \sqrt{3} \cdot 4 = 4\sqrt{3}$ in.

SOLUTION   In the triangle above, $b = 4$ inches and $a = 4\sqrt{3}$ inches.

EXAMPLE 3

The diagonal of a square measures 12 inches. What is the length of each side of the square?

STRATEGY   **Use what you know about special right triangles.**

STEP 1   Draw the square.

Since all sides of a square have the same length, label each side a. The diagonal divides the square into two right triangles. Because each right triangle has legs with the same length, each triangle is a 45°-45°-90° triangle.

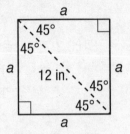

STEP 2   Use what you know about 45°-45°-90° triangles.

The diagonal is the hypotenuse, and the hypotenuse is $\sqrt{2}$ times the length of either leg, so:

$$12 = a \cdot \sqrt{2}$$

$$\frac{12}{\sqrt{2}} = a$$

Simplify so there is no radical in the denominator.

$$a = \frac{12}{\sqrt{2}} \cdot \frac{\sqrt{2}}{\sqrt{2}} = \frac{12\sqrt{2}}{(\sqrt{2})^2} = \frac{12\sqrt{2}}{2} = 6\sqrt{2} \text{ in.}$$

Use your calculator to approximate the length: $6\sqrt{2}$ in. $\approx$ 8.5 in.

SOLUTION   **The sides of the square are $6\sqrt{2}$ inches, or approximately 8.5 inches, long.**

COACHED EXAMPLE

What is the length of the shorter leg in this triangle?

$4\sqrt{3}$ cm

a

60°   30°

c

THINKING IT THROUGH

The length of the longer leg is _____ cm.

In a 30°-60°-90° triangle, the longer leg is _____ times the length of the shorter leg. Find the length of the shorter leg, a.

_____ = _____ · a

_____

_____

The length of the shorter leg is _____ centimeters.

Lesson Practice

Choose the correct answer.

Use this triangle for questions 1 and 2.

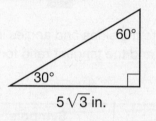

5√3 in.

1. What is the length of the shorter leg?

   A. 2.5 in.

   B. 5 in.

   C. 5√3 in.

   D. 10√3 in.

2. What is the length of the hypotenuse?

   A. 5 in.

   B. 5√3 in.

   C. 10 in.

   D. 10√3 in.

3. What is the length of the hypotenuse?

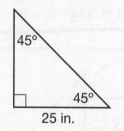

25 in.

   A. 12.5√2 in.

   B. 25√2 in.

   C. 25√3 in.

   D. 50 in.

4. What is the measure of the altitude of this equilateral triangle?

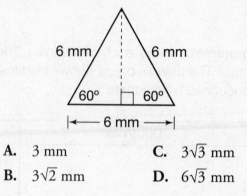

6 mm

   A. 3 mm   C. 3√3 mm

   B. 3√2 mm   D. 6√3 mm

Use this information for questions 5 and 6.

A telephone pole is attached to the ground with a guy wire as shown. The guy wire is secured to the ground 15 feet from the base of the pole.

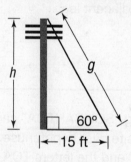

15 ft

5. What is the height of the pole, *h*?

   A. 7.5 ft

   B. 15√2 ft

   C. 15√3 ft

   D. 30 ft

6. What is the length of the guy wire, *g*?

   A. 7.5 ft

   B. 15√2 ft

   C. 15√3 ft

   D. 30 ft

25 Trigonometric Ratios

MM2G2.a, MM2G2.b

Trigonometry is the study of triangles. **Trigonometric ratios** relate the sides and angles in a right triangle. The triangle below shows the sine ratio, the cosine ratio, and the tangent ratio for angle θ (pronounced "angle theta").

Diagram	Ratio	Symbols
	The **sine** (sin) of an angle is the ratio of the length of the opposite leg to the length of the hypotenuse.	$\sin \theta = \dfrac{\text{opposite}}{\text{hypotenuse}}$
	The **cosine** (cos) of an angle is the ratio of the length of the adjacent leg to the length of the hypotenuse.	$\cos \theta = \dfrac{\text{adjacent}}{\text{hypotenuse}}$
	The **tangent** (tan) of an angle is the ratio of the length of the opposite leg to the length of the adjacent leg.	$\tan \theta = \dfrac{\text{opposite}}{\text{adjacent}}$ $\tan \theta = \dfrac{\sin \theta}{\cos \theta}$

(Diagram: right triangle labeled with *hypotenuse*, *opposite leg*, *adjacent leg*, and angle θ.)

Remembering "SOHCAHTOA" can help you recall these ratios. The letters SOH stand for "**s**ine equals **o**pposite over **h**ypotenuse," the letters CAH stand for "**c**osine equals **a**djacent over **h**ypotenuse," and the letters TOA stand for "**t**angent equals **o**pposite over **a**djacent."

You can use these ratios to find missing lengths or angle measures in right triangles.

EXAMPLE 1

Find the value of *x* in the triangle shown at the right.

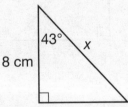

STRATEGY   **Use trigonometric ratios.**

STEP 1   Determine which ratio to use.

The 43° angle is the only angle measure given. The length of the leg adjacent to that angle, 8 cm, is also given. You need to find the length of the hypotenuse.

Use the cosine ratio, since that ratio uses the adjacent leg and the hypotenuse.

STEP 2   Set up the cosine ratio.

$$\cos 43° = \frac{\text{adjacent}}{\text{hypotenuse}} = \frac{8}{x}$$

STEP 3   Solve the equation for x.

$\cos 43° \cdot x = \frac{8}{x} \cdot x$ Multiply both sides by x.

$\cos 43° \cdot x = 8$

$\dfrac{\cos 43° \cdot x}{\cos 43°} = \dfrac{8}{\cos 43°}$ Divide both sides by $\cos 43°$.

Use your calculator to approximate $\cos 43°$.

$x \approx \dfrac{8}{0.731} \approx 10.9$ cm

SOLUTION   **The value of x is approximately 10.9 centimeters.**

Similar triangles have corresponding congruent angles and corresponding side lengths that are proportional. The symbol $\sim$ means "is similar to." The symbol $\cong$ means "is congruent to."

EXAMPLE 2

In the diagram below, $\triangle ABC \sim \triangle DEF$.

a. Explain the relationships between the angles of the similar triangles.

b. Explore the relationship between the trigonometric ratios of corresponding angles C and F. (Given: $m\angle C \approx 22.62°$.)

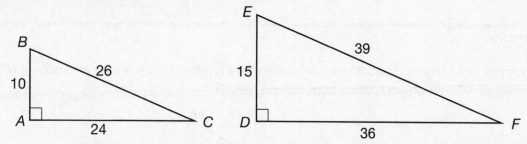

STRATEGY   **Explain the relationship between the angle measures and side lengths of the triangles. Look for comparable relationships among the trigonometric ratios.**

STEP 1   Identify the relationship between the angles of triangles ABC and DEF.

Corresponding angles of similar triangles are congruent, so:

$$m\angle A = m\angle D \quad\quad m\angle B = m\angle E \quad\quad m\angle C = m\angle F$$

STEP 2   Find the sine ratios for angles C and F.

$$\sin C = \frac{\text{opp}}{\text{hyp}} = \frac{10}{26} \approx 0.385$$

$$\sin F = \frac{\text{opp}}{\text{hyp}} = \frac{15}{39} \approx 0.385$$

$$\sin C = \sin F$$

STEP 3   Find the cosine and tangent ratios for angles C and F.

$$\cos C = \frac{adj}{hyp} = \frac{24}{26} \approx 0.923 \qquad \tan C = \frac{opp}{adj} = \frac{10}{24} \approx 0.417$$

$$\cos F = \frac{adj}{hyp} = \frac{36}{39} \approx 0.923 \qquad \tan F = \frac{opp}{adj} = \frac{15}{36} \approx 0.417$$

$$\cos C = \cos F \text{ and } \tan C = \tan F$$

If you found the trigonometric ratios for the other pairs of corresponding angles, you would discover the same relationship.

STEP 4   Why does this relationship exist?

Trigonometric ratios are constants. For example, the sine of any angle that measures $22.62° \approx 0.385$. So, the sine ratio for any two congruent angles will be equal. This is also true for cosines and tangents.

SOLUTION   **The measures of corresponding angles are equal. Because the measures of corresponding angles are equal, the trigonometric ratios for the corresponding angles are also equal.**

The trigonometric ratios of **complementary angles** are also related in a special way. The sum of the measures of two complementary angles is 90°. The two acute angles in a right triangle are always complementary because a right triangle has one 90° angle and the sum of the measures of the interior angles of any triangle is 180°. That means that the sum of the measures of two acute angles must be $180° − 90° = 90°$.

EXAMPLE 3

In right triangle JKL, angles J and K are complementary angles. Find the sine and cosine ratios for those two angles. What do you notice about those ratios?

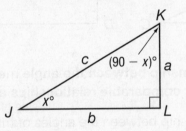

STRATEGY   **Find the sine and cosine of angles J and K. Compare them.**

STEP 1   Find $\sin J$ and $\cos J$.

$$\sin J = \sin x° = \frac{opp}{hyp} = \frac{a}{c}$$

$$\cos J = \cos x° = \frac{adj}{hyp} = \frac{b}{c}$$

STEP 2   Find sin K and cos K.

$$\sin K = \sin (90 - x)° = \frac{\text{opp}}{\text{hyp}} = \frac{b}{c}$$

$$\cos K = \cos (90 - x)° = \frac{\text{adj}}{\text{hyp}} = \frac{a}{c}$$

STEP 3   Compare the ratios.

The sine of angle J and the cosine of angle K are both equal to $\frac{a}{c}$.

The cosine of angle J and the sine of angle K are both equal to $\frac{b}{c}$.

SOLUTION   **For the complementary angles in the right triangle, $\sin x° = \cos (90 - x)°$ and vice versa. This will be true for any right triangle.**

COACHED EXAMPLE

Use your calculator to prove that this statement is true: $\sin Q - \cos R = 0$.

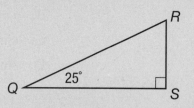

THINKING IT THROUGH

Angles Q and R are examples of _____ angles, so the sum of their measures is _____°.

Angle Q measures 25°.

The measure of angle R is: _____° − 25° = _____°.

Use your calculator to find the following:

$\sin Q = \sin 25° \approx$ _____

$\cos R = \cos$ _____° $\approx$ _____

Are those measures equal? _____

For any pair of complementary angles in a right triangle, the sine of one angle is _____ the cosine of the other angle.

So, if you subtract them, the difference will be equal to _____.

I proved that $\sin Q - \cos R = 0$ because $\sin Q$ is _____ to $\cos R$, and if _____ is subtracted from _____, the result will be _____.

Lesson Practice

Choose the correct answer.

Use the triangle below for questions 1 and 2.

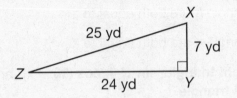

1. Which ratio is equivalent to sin Z?

    A. $\frac{7}{24}$

    B. $\frac{7}{25}$

    C. $\frac{24}{25}$

    D. $\frac{25}{7}$

2. Which ratio is equivalent to tan X?

    A. $\frac{7}{24}$

    B. $\frac{7}{25}$

    C. $\frac{24}{25}$

    D. $\frac{24}{7}$

3. Which is closest to the value of w?

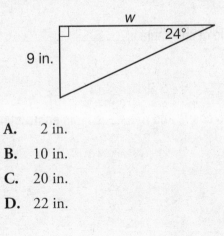

    A. 2 in.

    B. 10 in.

    C. 20 in.

    D. 22 in.

△**FGH** ~ △**KLM**. Use these triangles for questions 4–6.

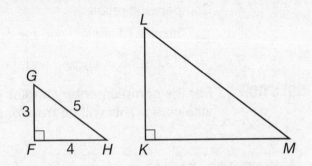

4. Which of the following must be true?

    A. tan G = tan L

    B. tan G = tan M

    C. sin H = tan L

    D. sin H = tan M

5. If sin $G = \frac{4}{5}$, then which of the following must also be true?

    A. sin $H = \frac{4}{5}$

    B. sin $K = \frac{4}{5}$

    C. sin $M = \frac{4}{5}$

    D. sin $L = \frac{4}{5}$

6. If sin $H = \frac{3}{5}$, then which of the following must also be true?

    A. sin $K = \frac{3}{5}$

    B. sin $L = \frac{3}{5}$

    C. cos $L = \frac{3}{5}$

    D. cos $M = \frac{3}{5}$

26 Solving Problems with Trigonometric Ratios

MM2G2.c, MM2P4.c, MM2P5.a, MM2P5.b, MM2P5.c

In the real world, you can sometimes measure lengths or heights directly. For example, if you wanted to know your height, you could measure it with a tape measure. However, what if an object is very large, such as a tree, or if it is difficult to measure directly, such as the distance across a river? In that case, you may be able to use trigonometric ratios to measure these objects indirectly. To review the trigonometric ratios, look back at Lesson 25.

EXAMPLE 1

The side of a building forms a 90° angle with the pavement. It casts a shadow as shown below.

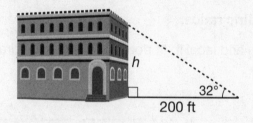

What is the height of the building to the nearest foot?

STRATEGY Use trigonometric ratios.

STEP 1 Determine which measurements you know.

One acute angle of the right triangle measures 32°.

The leg adjacent to that angle measures 200 feet.

The length of the leg opposite that angle, h, is unknown.

STEP 2 Identify the trigonometric ratio that you should use.

The tangent ratio uses the opposite and adjacent legs.

STEP 3 Find the height.

$$\tan 32° = \frac{\text{opp}}{\text{adj}} = \frac{h}{200}$$

$$(\tan 32°) \cdot 200 = h$$

$$125 \approx h$$

SOLUTION To the nearest foot, the height of the building is 125 feet.

When viewing an object from above or below, you can find distances indirectly by using the **angle of elevation** or the **angle of depression**. These two angles are congruent.

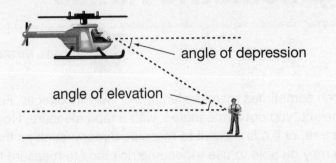

angle of depression

angle of elevation

EXAMPLE 2

A hot air balloon hovers above its launch site at an altitude of 510 feet. The balloon operator sees a playground at a 10° angle of depression. Estimate the ground distance between the launch site and the playground.

STRATEGY   Use trigonometric ratios.

STEP 1   Draw a diagram and label it. (It does not need to be drawn to scale.)

510 ft

10° — angle of depression

angle of elevation → 10°

d

Playground

The angle of depression and the angle of elevation are congruent, so label both of those angles 10°, as shown above.

The leg opposite the angle of elevation represents the altitude, which is 510 feet.

The leg adjacent to that angle represents the ground distance, *d*.

STEP 2   Identify the trigonometric ratio that you should use.

The tangent ratio uses the opposite and adjacent legs.

STEP 3   Find the height.

$$\tan 10° = \frac{\text{opp}}{\text{adj}} = \frac{510}{d}$$

$$(\tan 10°)(d) = 510$$

$$d = \frac{510}{\tan 10°} \approx 2,892$$

SOLUTION   **The ground distance between the launch site and the playground is approximately 2,892 feet.**

EXAMPLE 3

Shabana is building a skateboard ramp. She made the sketch to the right to show the height of the ramp and the angle from the ground to the top of the ramp. Shabana is cutting a board to use for the diagonal part of the ramp, labeled d. To the nearest inch, what should be the length of the board she cuts?

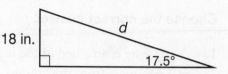

STRATEGY   Use trigonometric ratios.

STEP 1   Determine which ratio to use.

One acute angle of the right triangle measures 17.5°.

The leg opposite that angle measures 18 inches.

The length of the hypotenuse, d, is unknown.

The sine ratio uses the opposite leg and the hypotenuse.

STEP 2   Find the height.

$$\sin 17.5° = \frac{\text{opp}}{\text{hyp}} = \frac{18}{d}$$

$$(\sin 17.5°) \cdot d = 18$$

$$d = \frac{18}{\sin 17.5°} \approx 60 \text{ in.}$$

SOLUTION   **To the nearest inch, the length of the board should be 60 inches.**

COACHED EXAMPLE

A scientist's eye level is 6 feet above the ground. She measures the angle of elevation to the top of a tree to be 40°. The scientist is standing 100 feet from the tree. What is the height of the tree to the nearest foot?

THINKING IT THROUGH

One acute angle of the right triangle measures _____°. The leg _____ to that angle measures 100 feet.

The length of the leg _____ that angle is unknown and is labeled x.

The tangent ratio uses the _____ leg and the _____ leg.

$$\tan \underline{\hspace{1cm}}° = \frac{\text{opposite}}{\text{adjacent}} = \underline{\hspace{2cm}} = \underline{\hspace{3cm}}$$

To find the total height, add the value of x to the height of the scientist.

_____ + _____ = _____ feet

The height of the tree, to the nearest foot, is _____ feet.

Lesson Practice

Choose the correct answer.

1. A guy wire is attached to the top of a pole at a 63° angle from the ground. Which is closest to the height of the pole?

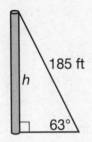

   A. 84 ft

   B. 165 ft

   C. 208 ft

   D. 363 ft

2. The top of a lighthouse is 80 feet above sea level. The angle of elevation from a fishing boat to the top of the lighthouse is 5°. Which is closest to the distance between the boat and the base of the lighthouse?

   A. 7 ft

   B. 80 ft

   C. 914 ft

   D. 927 ft

3. A package of food will be dropped from an airplane to a target on the ground, where a group of campers will retrieve it. The altitude of the plane is 700 meters. The angle of depression to the target is 15°. To the nearest meter, what is the horizontal ground distance on between the plane and the target?

   A. 188 m   C. 2,612 m

   B. 711 m   D. 4,031 m

4. A land surveyor created the diagram below to help her find the distance, *d*, from point *X* on the shore to point *Y* on an island in a lake. What is the distance to the nearest meter?

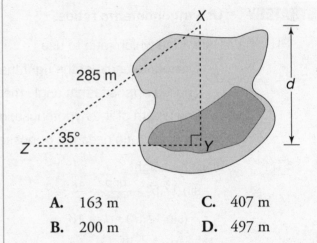

   A. 163 m   C. 407 m

   B. 200 m   D. 497 m

5. A blimp hovers at an altitude of 500 feet above a tennis stadium. The pilot of the blimp sights a creek at a 10° angle of depression. To the nearest foot, what is the horizontal distance between the creek and the stadium?

   A. 2,879 ft   C. 88 ft

   B. 2,836 ft   D. 86 ft

6. A student whose eye level is 5 feet above the ground measures the angle of elevation to the top of a flagpole as 29°. The student is standing approximately 162 feet from the base of the flagpole. What is the height of the flagpole to the nearest foot?

   A. 79 ft

   B. 85 ft

   C. 90 ft

   D. 95 ft

27 Central, Inscribed, and Other Angles

MM2G3.b, MM2G3.d

A circle is all the points in a plane that are equidistant from one point, the center. A circle is named by its center. An angle whose vertex is the center of the circle and whose two rays are **radii** of the circle is called a **central angle.** The **circumference** of a circle is the distance around the circle. A continuous part of the circle is called an **arc.** An arc contains two endpoints and all the points on the circle between those two points. Arcs can be measured in degrees.

The table below describes the different types of arcs and how to measure them.

The endpoints of a semicircle are the endpoints of a **diameter** of the circle. A **semicircle** is named using three points—its endpoints and one point between them. A semicircle takes up half the circumference, so its measure is always $\frac{1}{2}$ of 360°, or 180°.

Semicircles

$m\overset{\frown}{ABC} = 180°$

$m\overset{\frown}{ADC} = 180°$

A **minor arc** is smaller than a semicircle. It is named using only its two endpoints. Its measure is equal to the measure of its central angle.

A **major arc** is larger than a semicircle. It is named using three points: its two endpoints and one point between them. Its measure is equal to the total measure of the circle, 360°, minus the measure of the minor arc with the same endpoints.

Minor Arc

$m\overset{\frown}{EF} = m\angle EOF = x°$

Major Arc

$m\overset{\frown}{EGF} = (360 - x)°$

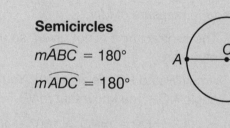

Theorems can help explain the relationships between geometric figures and prove statements to be true. Below are some theorems related to arcs and central angles that you should know.

The measure of the arc formed by two **adjacent arcs** is the sum of the measures of those two arcs.

In the same circle or in congruent circles, two minor arcs are congruent if and only if their central angles are congruent.

EXAMPLE 1

In circle O, $\overline{MQ}$ is a diameter. Find the measures of $\overarc{MN}$ and $\overarc{PQ}$ and use those measures to prove that the two arcs are congruent.

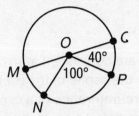

STRATEGY   Use what you know about the relationships between arcs and central angles.

STEP 1   Find the measure of $\overarc{PQ}$.

Its central angle, $\angle POQ$, measures $40°$, so $m\overarc{PQ} = 40°$.

STEP 2   Find the measure of $\overarc{MN}$.

The central angle is not given, so use what you know to determine the measure of the arc.

Arcs NP and PQ are adjacent. You know that $m\overarc{PQ} = 40°$. Based on central angle NOP, you know that $m\overarc{NP} = 100°$.

$m\overarc{NQ} = m\overarc{NP} + m\overarc{PQ} = 100° + 40° = 140°$

Arc MN is adjacent to $\overarc{NQ}$, so the sum of their measures is equal to the measure of $\overarc{MNQ}$, which is a semicircle.

Substitute $180°$ for $m\overarc{MNQ}$ and $140°$ for $m\overarc{NQ}$, and solve for $m\overarc{MN}$.

$m\overarc{MNQ} = m\overarc{MN} + m\overarc{NQ}$

$\quad 180° = m\overarc{MN} + 140°$

$\quad\ \ 40° = m\overarc{MN}$

STEP 3   Determine if the two arcs are congruent.

$m\overarc{MN} = 40°$ and $m\overarc{PQ} = 40°$, so, $\overarc{MN} \cong \overarc{PQ}$.

SOLUTION   Both $\overarc{MN}$ and $\overarc{PQ}$ measure $40°$, so they are congruent arcs.

An angle whose vertex is on a circle and whose sides contain **chords** of the circle is called an **inscribed angle**. The sides of the inscribed angle will form the endpoints of an arc. That arc is called the **intercepted arc**.

Below are important theorems and corollaries to know about inscribed angles:

The measure of an inscribed angle is equal to half the measure of its intercepted arc.

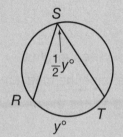

$$m\angle RST = \frac{1}{2}m\widehat{RT}$$

If two inscribed angles intercept the same arc, then the angles are congruent.

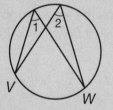

Both angles 1 and 2 intercept $\widehat{VW}$, so $\angle 1 \cong \angle 2$.

An inscribed angle that intercepts a semicircle is a right angle.

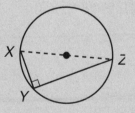

$\widehat{XYZ}$ is a semicircle, so $m\angle XYZ = 90°$.

If a quadrilateral is inscribed in a circle, then its opposite angles are **supplementary**.

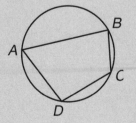

$$m\angle A + m\angle C = 180°$$
$$m\angle B + m\angle D = 180°$$

EXAMPLE 2

Find the measure of $\overset{\frown}{FG}$ in the circle below.

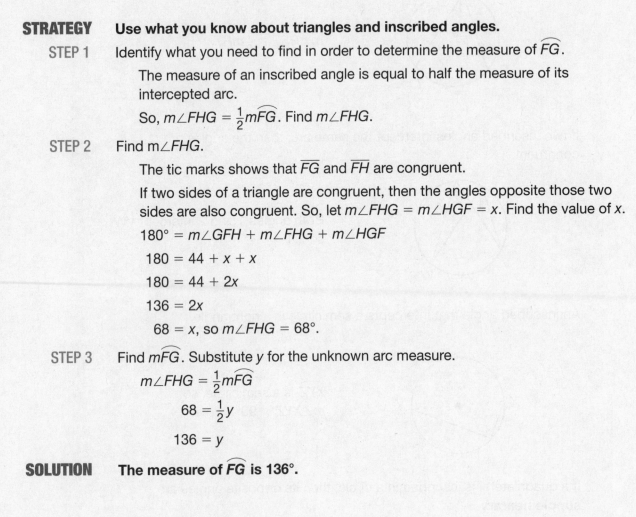

STRATEGY Use what you know about triangles and inscribed angles.

STEP 1 Identify what you need to find in order to determine the measure of $\overset{\frown}{FG}$.

The measure of an inscribed angle is equal to half the measure of its intercepted arc.

So, $m\angle FHG = \frac{1}{2}m\overset{\frown}{FG}$. Find $m\angle FHG$.

STEP 2 Find $m\angle FHG$.

The tic marks shows that $\overline{FG}$ and $\overline{FH}$ are congruent.

If two sides of a triangle are congruent, then the angles opposite those two sides are also congruent. So, let $m\angle FHG = m\angle HGF = x$. Find the value of x.

$180° = m\angle GFH + m\angle FHG + m\angle HGF$

$180 = 44 + x + x$

$180 = 44 + 2x$

$136 = 2x$

$68 = x$, so $m\angle FHG = 68°$.

STEP 3 Find $m\overset{\frown}{FG}$. Substitute y for the unknown arc measure.

$m\angle FHG = \frac{1}{2}m\overset{\frown}{FG}$

$68 = \frac{1}{2}y$

$136 = y$

SOLUTION The measure of $\overset{\frown}{FG}$ is 136°.

You should also know about the angles formed by chords, **secants**, and **tangents**. For more information about chords, secants, and tangents, look ahead to Lesson 28.

The measure of an angle formed by a chord and a tangent that meet at the **point of tangency** is equal to half the measure of the intercepted arc.

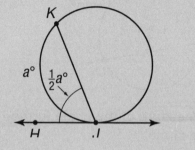

$$m\angle HJK = \tfrac{1}{2}m\widehat{KJ}$$

The measure of the angle formed when two chords or secants intersect inside a circle is equal to half the sum of the measures of its intercepted arcs.

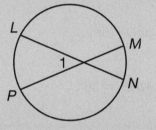

$$m\angle 1 = \tfrac{1}{2}(m\widehat{LP} + m\widehat{MN})$$

The measure of an angle formed by two secants, two tangents, or a secant and a tangent drawn from a point outside the circle is equal to half the difference of the measures of the intercepted arcs.

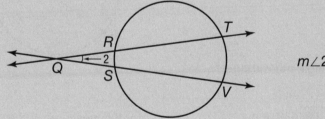

$$m\angle 2 = \tfrac{1}{2}(m\widehat{TV} - m\widehat{RS})$$

EXAMPLE 3

Ray *NM* is tangent to circle *L* at point *M* and $\overline{NQ}$ is a secant. Find the value of *y*.

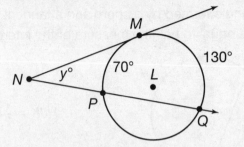

STRATEGY Use what you know about the measure of the angle formed by a secant and a tangent drawn from outside the circle.

STEP 1 Identify what you know about the measure of ∠*y*.

The secant and tangent are drawn from the same point outside the circle.

$$m\angle MNP = \tfrac{1}{2}(\overset{\frown}{mMQ} - \overset{\frown}{mMP})$$

STEP 2 Substitute the given measures and solve for *y*.

$$y = \tfrac{1}{2}(130 - 70) = \tfrac{1}{2}(60) = 30$$

SOLUTION The value of *y* is 30, because *m*∠*MNP* = 30°.

COACHED EXAMPLE

Line segments *DF* and *EG* are chords of the circle to the right.

Find the values of *y* and *z*.

THINKING IT THROUGH

Find the value of *y*.

Chords *DF* and *EG* intersect to form the angle measuring *y*°.

The intercepted arcs are _____ and _____.

The measure of the angle formed is equal to half of the _____ of the measures of the intercepted arcs. Substitute the degree measures of the given arcs and solve.

$$y = \tfrac{1}{2}(\text{_____}) = \tfrac{1}{2}(\text{\_\_\_\_\_}) = \text{_____}$$

Find the value of *z*.

The angle labeled *z*° was formed by chords *DF* and *EG* and intercepts arcs _____ and _____.

Since the angle labeled *z*° is formed by the same _____ as the angle labeled *y*° and intercepts the same _____ as the angle labeled *y*°, *z* = *y* = _____.

Both *y* and *z* have a value of _____.

Lesson Practice

Choose the correct answer.

Use circle O for questions 1 and 2.

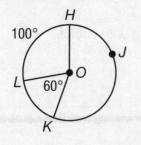

1. What is the measure of ∠*LOH*?

   A. 50°   C. 100°

   B. 60°   D. 160°

2. What is the measure of $\widehat{HJK}$?

   A. 130°   C. 260°

   B. 200°   D. 300°

Use this circle for questions 3 and 4.

In the circle below, $m\widehat{SN} = 30°$, $m\widehat{RS} = 94°$, and $m\widehat{QP} = 62°$.

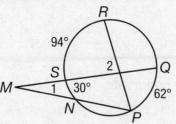

3. What is the measure of ∠1?

   A. 16°   C. 62°

   B. 46°   D. 78°

4. What is the measure of ∠2?

   A. 16°   C. 78°

   B. 32°   D. 156°

Use this circle for questions 5–7.

In the circle below, $\overline{AB}$ is tangent to the circle at point *B*.

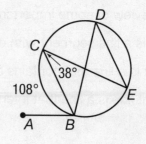

5. What is the measure of ∠*ABC*?

   A. 54°   C. 108°

   B. 76°   D. 216°

6. What is the measure of ∠*BDE*?

   A. 76°   C. 38°

   B. 54°   D. 19°

7. What is the measure of $\widehat{BE}$?

   A. 19°   C. 73°

   B. 38°   D. 76°

8. In the circle shown below, $m\angle SVR = 90°$ and $m\widehat{SR} = 120°$.

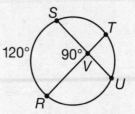

   What is the measure of $\widehat{TU}$?

   A. 30°   C. 90°

   B. 60°   D. 120°

28 Chords, Tangents, and Secants

MM2G3.a, MM2G3.b, MM2G3.d, MM2P2.a, MM2P2.b, MM2P2.c, MM2P2.d, MM2P3.c

Below is a review of some important terms to know when working with circles.

- A chord is a line segment with endpoints on the circle.

- A secant is a line that contains a chord.

- A tangent line is a line that intersects a circle in exactly one point, called the point of tangency.

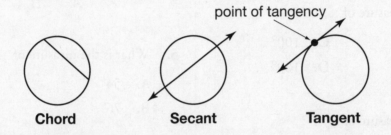

point of tangency

Chord   **Secant**   **Tangent**

Three theorems involving the properties of chords, tangents, and secants are described below.

A tangent line and a radius drawn to the point of tangency are perpendicular.

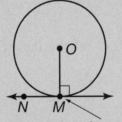

$\overline{OM} \perp \overleftrightarrow{NM}$

point of tangency

Tangents to a circle drawn from the same point are congruent.

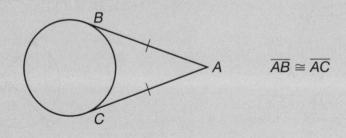

$\overline{AB} \cong \overline{AC}$

In the same circle or in congruent circles:

(a) congruent arcs have congruent chords, and

(b) congruent chords have congruent arcs.

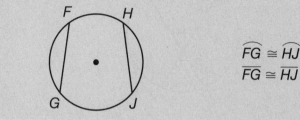

$\overset{\frown}{FG} \cong \overset{\frown}{HJ}$

$\overline{FG} \cong \overline{HJ}$

EXAMPLE 1

Circle O is inscribed in $\triangle HIJ$. Find the perimeter of $\triangle HIJ$.

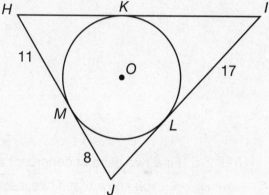

STRATEGY   **Use what you know about tangents drawn from points outside a circle.**

STEP 1   Name the theorems or properties that will help you solve this problem.

If two segments are tangent to a circle from the same point outside the circle, they are congruent.

STEP 2   Use that theorem to find congruent segments and determine missing lengths.

$\overline{HM} \cong \overline{HK}$. If $HM = 11$, then $HK = 11$.

$\overline{JM} \cong \overline{JL}$. If $JM = 8$, then $JL = 8$.

$\overline{IK} \cong \overline{IL}$. If $IL = 17$, then $IK = 17$.

STEP 3   Find the perimeter, P.

$P = HJ + JI + HI = (11 + 8) + (8 + 17) + (17 + 11) = 72$ units

SOLUTION   **The perimeter is 72 units.**

Below is another theorem you should know about the lengths of chords.

If two chords intersect inside a circle, then the product of the segments of one chord equals the product of the segments of the other chord.

EXAMPLE 2

In the circle below, $\overline{WY}$ and $\overline{XZ}$ intersect at point P. Prove that $ab = cd$.

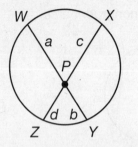

STRATEGY **Use geometric theorems and properties to prove that the product of the segments of one chord equals the product of the segments of the other chord.**

STEP 1 Draw chords $\overline{WZ}$ and $\overline{XY}$ using dashed lines.

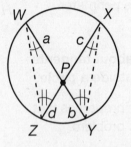

STEP 2 Find two pairs of congruent angles in the triangles formed.

You know that if two inscribed angles intercept the same arc, they are congruent.

Angles ZWY and ZXY both intercept $\overset{\frown}{ZY}$: $\angle ZWY \cong \angle ZXY$.

Angles WZX and WYX both intercept $\overset{\frown}{WX}$: $\angle WZX \cong \angle WYX$.

STEP 3 Prove that the two triangles formed are similar.

Two angles in $\triangle WPZ$ are congruent to two angles in $\triangle XPY$. Since the sum of the measures of the angles of both triangles is 180°, the third angles must also be congruent. $\triangle WPZ \sim \triangle XPY$

STEP 4 Identity the relationship among the side lengths of the similar triangles.

Similar triangles have corresponding side lengths in the same proportion, so $\frac{a}{c} = \frac{d}{b}$.

STEP 5 Cross-multiply.

$$\frac{a}{c} = \frac{d}{b}$$
$$ab = cd$$

SOLUTION **The steps above prove that $ab = cd$ in the given circle.**

You can also apply what you know about triangle similarity to prove that the following theorem is true.

> When two secant segments are drawn to a circle from a point outside the circle, the product of one secant segment and its external segment equals the product of the other secant segment and its external segment.

EXAMPLE 3

In the circle to the right, $\overline{PJ}$ and $\overline{PM}$ are secants drawn from point P. The length of $PJ = a$ and the length of $PM = c$. The length of $KP = b$ and the length of $LP = d$. Prove that $ab = cd$.

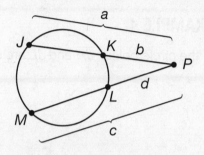

STRATEGY   Use geometric theorems and properties to prove that the product of the length of one secant segment and its external segment equals the product of the length of the other secant segment and its external segment.

STEP 1   Draw chords $\overline{JM}$ and $\overline{KL}$.

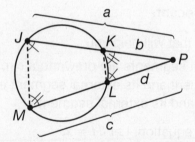

STEP 2   Find two pairs of congruent angles in the triangles formed.

Quadrilateral $JKLM$ is inscribed in the circle.

Opposite angles MJK and KLM are supplementary.

Angles KLM and KLP lie on the same line, so they are also supplementary.

Since angles MJK and KLP are each supplementary to $\angle KLM$, $\angle MJK \cong \angle KLP$.

Opposite angles JML and JKL are supplementary, and angles JKL and PKL are also supplementary. So, $\angle JML \cong \angle PKL$.

STEP 3   Prove that the two triangles formed are similar.

Two angles in $\triangle PJM$ are congruent to two angles in $\triangle PLK$.

Those two triangles share a third angle, which could be named either $\angle JPM$ or $\angle KPL$. So, three angles of $\triangle PJM$ are congruent to three angles of $\triangle PLK$.

$\triangle PJM \sim \triangle PLK$

STEP 4   Identity the relationship among the side lengths of the similar triangles.

$$\frac{PJ}{PL} = \frac{PM}{PK} = \frac{a}{d} = \frac{c}{b}$$

STEP 5   Cross-multiply.

$$\frac{a}{d} = \frac{c}{b}$$
$$ab = cd$$

SOLUTION   **The steps above prove that $ab = cd$ in the given circle.**

EXAMPLE 4

In the circle below, $\overline{JH}$ and $\overline{JL}$ are secants drawn from point J. What is the length of $\overline{IH}$?

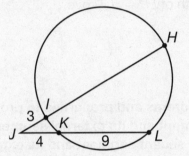

STRATEGY   **Use theorems and properties to determine the length of IH, which is the length of a segment of a secant.**

STEP 1   Identify the theorem that will help you.

When two secant segments are drawn to a circle from a point, the product of one secant segment and its external segment equals the product of the other secant segment and its external segment.

STEP 2   Set up and solve an equation. Let $IH = x$.

$(JH)(JI) = (JL)(JK)$

The factors do not include IH. Rewrite the equation so IH is included.

$(JI + IH)(JI) = (JK + KL)(JK)$

$(3 + x)(3) = (4 + 9)(4)$

$9 + 3x = 52$

$3x = 43$

$x = 14\frac{1}{3}$

SOLUTION   **The length of IH is $14\frac{1}{3}$ units.**

When a secant segment and a tangent segment are drawn to a circle from a point outside the circle, the product of the secant segment and its external segment equals the square of the tangent segment.

COACHED EXAMPLE

In the diagram below, $\overline{PR}$ is a secant drawn to the circle from point P and $\overline{PT}$ is tangent to the circle at point T. Sam is trying to prove that $ab = c^2$. Help him by filling in the blanks in his proof below.

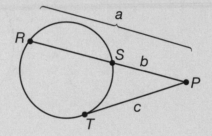

THINKING IT THROUGH

Draw chords $\overline{RT}$ and $\overline{ST}$ on the circle above.

Prove that $\triangle TRP$ is similar to $\triangle STP$ by finding two pairs of congruent angles.

Prove $\angle TRP \cong \angle STP$.

Inscribed $\angle TRP$ has a measure that is equal to $\frac{1}{2}$ of the measure of arc _____.

Angle STP is formed by chord _____ and tangent _____, so its measure is equal to $\frac{1}{2}$ of the measure of arc _____.

This means that $m\angle TRP = m\angle STP = \frac{1}{2}m$_____.

Those two angles are therefore congruent. Mark them as congruent on the diagram above.

Prove $\angle TPR \cong \angle SPT$.

$\angle TPR$ and $\angle SPT$ are two names for the _____ angle. Therefore, they are congruent.

Since you know that two angles in $\angle TRP$ are congruent to two angles in $\angle STP$, those triangles are _____.

How are the side lengths of the similar triangles related?

$\frac{RP}{TP} = \frac{PT}{} = \frac{a}{c} =$ _____

Cross-multiply. _____ $=$ _____

_____ $= c^2$

As proven above, the product of the secant segment, _____, and its external segment, _____, equals the square of the tangent segment, _____.

Lesson Practice

Choose the correct answer.

1. Line segment *HF* is tangent to circle *G* at point *F*.

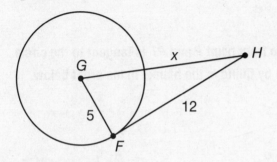

What is the value of *x*?

- **A.** 10
- **B.** 11
- **C.** 12
- **D.** 13

2. What is the approximate length of *MN*?

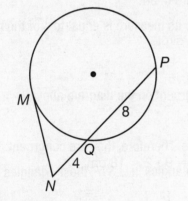

- **A.** 5.6 units
- **B.** 6.9 units
- **C.** 16 units
- **D.** 24 units

Use this diagram for questions 3 and 4.

In the diagram below, $\overline{IJ}$ is tangent to circles *F* and *M* at point *J*. Line segments *IG* and *IL* are secants.

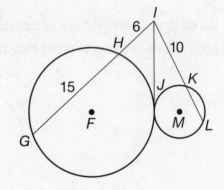

3. What is the approximate length of *IJ*?

- **A.** 8.8 units
- **B.** 10.6 units
- **C.** 11.2 units
- **D.** 16 units

4. What is the approximate length of *KL*?

- **A.** 2.6 units
- **B.** 3.4 units
- **C.** 4.1 units
- **D.** 12.6 units

5. What is the value of *z*?

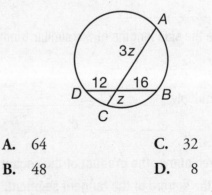

- **A.** 64
- **B.** 48
- **C.** 32
- **D.** 8

29 Arc Length and Sector Area

MM2G3.c, MM2G3.d, MM2P4.b, MM2P4.c

In Lesson 27, you learned that an arc can be measured in degrees. The length of an arc can also be measured in linear units such as inches or centimeters. Remember, an arc is part of the circumference of a circle. So, you can use the measure of an arc and the formula for the circumference of a circle to find an arc length.

EXAMPLE 1

What is the length of $\overset{\frown}{YZ}$?

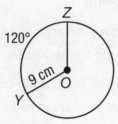

STRATEGY   **Use proportional reasoning.**

STEP 1   Write the formula for finding the circumference of a circle.

$C = \pi d$, where d stands for the diameter.

STEP 2   Relate the arc length to the circumference of circle O.

The measure of $\overset{\frown}{YZ}$ is 120°. The entire circle measures 360°.

$\frac{120}{360} = \frac{1}{3}$, so the length of $\overset{\frown}{YZ}$ is $\frac{1}{3}$ of the entire circumference.

STEP 3   Find the length of the arc.

Use the circumference formula, but multiply it by $\frac{1}{3}$.

Since the diameter is twice the radius, $d = 9 \cdot 2 = 18$ cm.

$m\overset{\frown}{YZ} = \frac{1}{3}(\pi d) = \left(\frac{1}{3} \cdot 18\right)\pi = 6\pi$ cm

SOLUTION   **The arc length is 6π cm.**

A **sector** of a circle is a region of a circle with two radii and an arc as its boundaries. In the circle below, radii *OA* and *OB*, and $\overset{\frown}{AB}$, form the boundaries of the shaded sector. This sector can be named sector *AOB*.

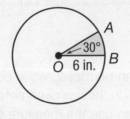

EXAMPLE 2

What is the area of shaded sector *AOB* shown above?

STRATEGY   **Use proportional reasoning.**

STEP 1   Write the formula for finding the area of a circle.

$A = \pi r^2$, where *r* stands for the radius.

STEP 2   Relate the sector area to the area of the circle above.

The measure of the central angle is 30°. The entire circle measures 360°.

$\frac{30}{360} = \frac{1}{12}$, so the area of the shaded sector is $\frac{1}{12}$ of the area of Circle *O*.

STEP 3   Find the area, *A*, of the sector.

Use the area formula, but multiply it by $\frac{1}{12}$.

$A = \frac{1}{12}(\pi r^2) = \left(\frac{1}{12} \cdot 6^2\right)\pi = \left(\frac{1}{12} \cdot 36\right)\pi = 3\pi$ in.^{2}

SOLUTION   **The area of the shaded sector is 3π in.^{2}**

In Examples 1 and 2, you used proportional reasoning to find an arc length and a sector area. The methods used in those examples can be used to derive the formulas below.

If an arc or a central angle measures $q°$, you can find the length of the arc and the area of the sector bounded by that arc using these formulas:

arc length $= \frac{q}{360} \cdot \pi d$

area of sector $= \frac{q}{360} \cdot \pi r^2$

EXAMPLE 3

A dog is leashed to the corner of a rectangular barn as shown below. Approximately how much area does the dog have to run around?

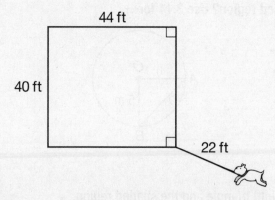

STRATEGY   **Sketch the area in which the dog can run. Then use proportional reasoning to find the area.**

STEP 1   Sketch the area in which the dog can run.

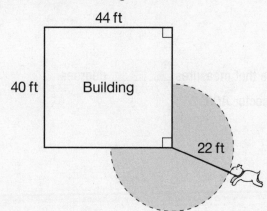

The sketch above shows a sector of a circle. The length of the leash is its radius.

STEP 2   Find the measure of the angle.

The corners of the building are right angles, which measure 90°.

So, subtract: 360° − 90° = 270°

STEP 3   Use the formula to find the area of the sector.

Since you need to find the approximate area, substitute 3.14 for π.

$$\text{area of sector} = \frac{q}{360} \cdot \pi r^2 \approx \frac{270}{360} \cdot (3.14)(22)^2$$

$$\approx \frac{270}{360} \cdot (3.14)(484) \approx 1{,}139.82$$

SOLUTION   **The dog has about 1,140 square feet of running space.**

COACHED EXAMPLE

What is the area of the shaded region? Use 3.14 for π.

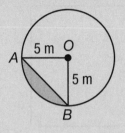

THINKING IT THROUGH

Sector *AOB* is made up of a right triangle and the shaded region.

The right triangle has a base length of _____ meters and a height of _____ m.

Find the area of a triangle.

A = _____

= _____

= _____

Sector *AOB* has a central angle that measures _____ degrees.

Find the approximate area of sector *AOB*.

A = _____

≈ _____

≈ _____

≈ _____

To find the area of the shaded region, subtract the area of the _____ _____ from the area of
the _____.

Area of shaded region ≈ _____ − _____ ≈ _____ m²

The area of the shaded region is approximately _____ square meters.

Lesson Practice

Choose the correct answer.

Use circle *O* for questions 1 and 2.

1. What is the length of $\overset{\frown}{MN}$?

   A. 1.5π yd

   B. 3π yd

   C. 10π yd

   D. 20π yd

2. What is the area of the shaded sector?

   A. 15π yd^2

   B. 25π yd^2

   C. 47π yd^2

   D. 85π yd^2

3. What is the length of $\overset{\frown}{GAH}$ in circle *O* below?

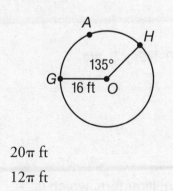

   A. 20π ft

   B. 12π ft

   C. 10π ft

   D. 6π ft

Use circle *X* for questions 4 and 5.

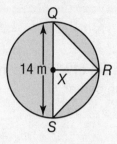

4. What is the approximate length of $\overset{\frown}{QR}$?

   A. 11 m

   B. 22 m

   C. 44 m

   D. 77 m

5. What is the approximate area of the shaded region of circle *X*?

   A. 14 m^2

   B. 28 m^2

   C. 77 m^2

   D. 105 m^2

6. The sprinkler system shown below has a spray of 15 feet and is set to rotate 100°. What is the approximate area of grass that will be watered by the sprinkler?

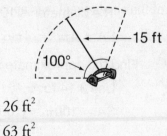

   A. 26 ft^2

   B. 63 ft^2

   C. 196 ft^2

   D. 785 ft^2

30 Surface Area and Volume of Spheres

MM2G4.a

A sphere is the set of all points in three-dimensional space that are located at a distance r, the radius, from the center, C.

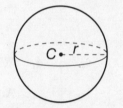

The surface area of a solid figure is the number of square units needed to cover all the surfaces of the figure. The formula for finding the surface area, SA, of a sphere is shown below.

$$SA = 4\pi r^2,$$
where $\pi \approx 3.14$ and r stands for the radius.

EXAMPLE 1

Find the surface area of the sphere below in terms of π. Then find the surface area of the same sphere using an approximation for π.

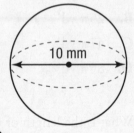

STRATEGY Use the formula for finding the surface area of a sphere.

STEP 1 Find the surface area in terms of π.

The radius is $\frac{1}{2}$ the diameter.

The diameter is 10 mm, so the radius is: $r = 10 \div 2 = 5$ mm.

$SA = 4\pi r^2 = 4\pi(5^2) = 4\pi(25) = 100\pi$ mm^2

STEP 2 Find the approximate surface area.

Use 3.14 for π.

$SA = 100\pi \approx (100)(3.14) \approx 314$ mm^2

SOLUTION **The surface area of the sphere is 100π square millimeters, which is approximately 314 square millimeters.**

The volume of a solid figure is the number of cubic units enclosed in the figure. The volume, V, of a sphere can be found using this formula:

$$V = \frac{4}{3}\pi r^3,$$

where $\pi \approx 3.14$ and r stands for the radius.

EXAMPLE 2

A candle company uses spherical molds to create their best-selling holiday candles. Each finished candle has a diameter of 4 inches. The company will produce 3,000 blue candles for their holiday inventory. Approximately how many cubic inches of blue wax will the company need to purchase?

STRATEGY   **Find the number of cubic inches of wax in one candle. Then multiply to find the number of cubic inches needed to make 3,000 candles.**

STEP 1   Find the number of cubic inches of wax needed to make one candle.

The diameter is 4 inches, so the radius is: $r = 4 \div 2 = 2$ in.

Substitute 3.14 for π and 2 for r into the formula and calculate the volume:

$V = \frac{4}{3}\pi r^3 \approx \frac{4}{3}(3.14)(2^3) \approx \frac{4}{3}(3.14)(8) \approx 33.5$ in.^{3}

STEP 2   Multiply the volume of one candle by the total number of candles needed.

The company wants to produce 3,000 blue candles.

$33.5 \cdot 3,000 = 100,500$ in.^{3}

SOLUTION   **The company will need 100,500 cubic inches of blue wax.**

Sometimes, you may need to think about which formulas to use and you may need to use more than one of them. It may help to look at the Mathematics II Formula Sheet. It will look like the sheet on page 265 of this book.

EXAMPLE 3

Find the approximate surface area and volume of this **hemisphere**.

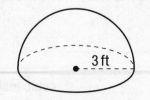

3 ft

STRATEGY   **Decide which formula will help you find the surface area and which will help you find the volume. Then find each.**

STEP 1   Which formula will help you find the surface area?

A hemisphere is half of a sphere. So, use the formula for finding the surface area of a sphere, but multiply by $\frac{1}{2}$.

STEP 2   Find the approximate surface area of the hemisphere.

surface area of curved part: $SA = \frac{1}{2}(4\pi r^2) \approx \frac{1}{2}(4 \cdot 3.14 \cdot 3^2) \approx \frac{1}{2}(4 \cdot 3.14 \cdot 9)$

$$\approx \frac{1}{2}(113.04) \approx 56.52 \text{ ft}^2$$

area of circular base: $A = \pi r^2 \approx (3.14)(3^2) \approx 28.26 \text{ ft}^2$

Total surface area $\approx 56.52 + 28.26 \approx 84.78 \text{ ft}^2$

STEP 3   Find the volume of the hemisphere.

A hemisphere is half of a sphere. So, its volume is half that of a sphere with the same radius.

$$V = \frac{1}{2}\left(\frac{4}{3}\pi r^3\right) \approx \frac{1}{2}\left(\frac{4}{3} \cdot 3.14 \cdot 3^3\right) \approx \frac{1}{2}\left(\frac{4}{3} \cdot 3.14 \cdot 27\right) \approx \frac{1}{2}(113.04) \approx 56.52 \text{ ft}^3$$

SOLUTION   **The hemisphere has a total surface area of approximately 84.78 square feet and a volume of approximately 56.52 square feet.**

COACHED EXAMPLE

The surface area of a sphere is 144π square meters. What is the volume of the sphere?

THINKING IT THROUGH

The formula for finding the surface area of a sphere is $SA = $ _____.

Substitute the known surface area for SA in the formula. Solve the equation for the radius, r.

_____ $=$ _____

_____

_____

_____ $= r$

The formula for finding the volume of a sphere is $V = $ _____.

Substitute the value of r you found above into that formula and find the volume.

$V = $ _____

$= $ _____

The volume of the sphere is _____ cubic meters.

Lesson Practice

Choose the correct answer.

1. What is the approximate surface area of a sphere with a diameter of 14 centimeters?

   A. 1,436.03 cm^2

   B. 615.44 cm^2

   C. 351.68 cm^2

   D. 87.92 cm^2

2. What is the approximate volume of a sphere with a radius of 11 inches?

   A. 44,580 in.^{3}

   B. 16,717 in.^{3}

   C. 15,198 in.^{3}

   D. 5,572 in.^{3}

3. The surface area of a sphere is 576π meters. What is the radius of the sphere?

   A. 12 m

   B. 21 m

   C. 72 m

   D. 144 m

4. The volume of a sphere is 4,500π cubic yards. What is the approximate diameter of the sphere?

   A. 116 yd

   B. 58 yd

   C. 30 yd

   D. 15 yd

5. The surface area of a sphere is 324π m^2. What is the volume of the sphere?

   A. 9π m^3

   B. 524π m^3

   C. 972π m^3

   D. 1,082π m^3

6. A pastry chef uses spherical molds to make solid chocolate candies. Each candy has a diameter of 3 centimeters. If the chef makes 1,500 cubic centimeters of melted chocolate, what is the maximum number of candies she can make?

   A. 13   **C.** 358

   B. 106   **D.** 500

7. A spherical ball is placed in a cube-shaped box as pictured below. The sphere touches the edge of the box on all sides.

   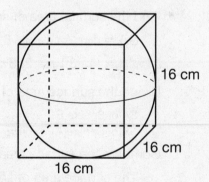

   To the nearest cubic centimeter, what is the volume of the empty space in the box?

   A. 856 cm^3

   B. 1,952 cm^3

   C. 2,144 cm^3

   D. 4,096 cm^3

31 Effects of Changing Dimensions of Spheres

MM2G4.b, MM2P1.a, MM2P1.c

When you change the radius or diameter of a sphere, the surface area and volume will change, too. Suppose you double the radius of a sphere. You may think that the surface area will also be doubled, but this is not the case because the formula for finding the surface area of a sphere involves squaring the radius. Example 1 shows what happens to the surface area of a sphere when you double its radius.

EXAMPLE 1

The radius of Sphere A was doubled to create Sphere B. Compare the surface area of sphere B to the surface area of sphere A. Then make a conjecture about how doubling the radius affects the surface area of a sphere.

STRATEGY   **Find the surface area of each sphere.**
Compare the two surface areas.
Make a conjecture.

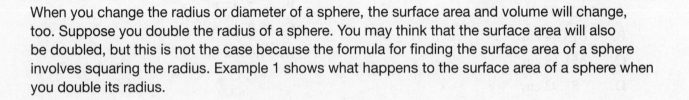

Sphere A   Sphere B

STEP 1   Find the surface area of sphere A.

$$SA = 4\pi r^2 = 4 \cdot \pi \cdot 4^2$$
$$= (4 \cdot 4^2)\pi = 64\pi \text{ square units}$$

STEP 2   Find the surface area of sphere B.

$$SA = 4\pi r^2 = 4 \cdot \pi \cdot 8^2$$
$$= (4 \cdot 8^2)\pi = 256\pi \text{ square units}$$

STEP 3   Divide the surface area of sphere B by the surface area of Sphere A.

$$\frac{SA \text{ of Sphere B}}{SA \text{ of Sphere A}} = \frac{256\pi}{64\pi} = 4$$

STEP 4   Compare the surface areas and make a conjecture.

The surface area of sphere B is 4 times the surface area of sphere A.

My conjecture is: Doubling the radius of a sphere makes its surface area 4 times greater.

SOLUTION   **Since the surface area of sphere B is 4 times greater than that of sphere A, my conjecture is: Doubling the radius makes the surface area 4 times greater.**

Note: The conjecture in Example 1 is true. You can try doubling the radii of different spheres to test it.

In the formula for finding the surface area of a sphere, the radius is squared. So, when the radius is increased by a factor of 2, the surface area is increased by a factor of 2^2, or 4. This will be true for any factor, k.

> If you multiply the radius or diameter of a sphere by a factor of k:
>
> - the surface area will change by a factor of k^2, and
>
> - the volume will change by a factor of k^3.

If the radius or diameter is not given in a problem, you can pick numbers to help you understand how the surface area or volume changes.

EXAMPLE 2

The radius of a sphere is quadrupled. What will be the effect on the volume of the sphere?

STRATEGY   **Pick numbers and test them in the original sphere and the new sphere. Then compare.**

STEP 1   Pick numbers for the radius.

Since the formula for finding the volume of a sphere includes a fraction with a 3 in the denominator, choose a multiple of 3, such as 6, for r.

STEP 2   Find the volume of the original sphere.
$$V = \frac{4}{3}\pi r^3 = \frac{4}{3} \cdot \pi \cdot 6^3 = \left(\frac{4}{3} \cdot 6^3\right)\pi = \left(\frac{4}{3} \cdot 216\right)\pi = 288\pi \text{ cubic units}$$

STEP 3   Find the radius of the new sphere.

The radius is quadrupled. So, if the original radius is 6, the new radius is:
$r = 6 \cdot 4 = 24$.

Find the volume of the new sphere.
$$V = \frac{4}{3}\pi r^3 = \frac{4}{3} \cdot \pi \cdot 24^3 = \left(\frac{4}{3} \cdot 24^3\right)\pi = \left(\frac{4}{3} \cdot 13{,}824\right)\pi = 18{,}432\pi \text{ cubic units}$$

STEP 4   Divide the new volume by the old volume to see how many times greater it is.
$$\frac{18{,}432\pi}{288\pi} = 64$$

STEP 5   Compare your results with the statements in the textbox.

The new volume is 64 times the original volume.

The statement in the box above says that when the radius is increased by a factor of k, the volume increases by a factor of k^3.

The radius is increased by a factor of 4, and the volume increases by a factor of 4^3 or 64.

SOLUTION   **The new volume is 4^3, or 64, times the original volume.**

COACHED EXAMPLE

The diameter of sphere A was multiplied by a factor of $\frac{1}{3}$ to create sphere B.

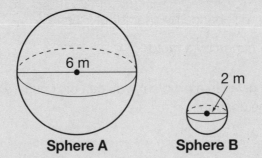

Sphere A   Sphere B

How does multiplying the diameter by $\frac{1}{3}$ change the volume?

THINKING IT THROUGH

Find the volume of sphere A.

The diameter is _____, so the radius is _____.

$V = \frac{4}{3} \cdot \pi \cdot ($_____$)^3 = $ _____

  $= $ _____

Find the volume of sphere B.

The diameter is _____, so the radius is _____.

$V = \frac{4}{3} \cdot \pi \cdot ($_____$)^3 = $ _____

  $= $ _____

Write the ratio of the new volume of sphere B to the original volume of sphere A.

_____

When the diameter is multiplied by a factor of $\frac{1}{3}$, the volume of the new sphere, sphere B, is _____ of the volume of the original sphere, sphere A.

Lesson Practice

Choose the correct answer.

Use the spheres below for questions 1 and 2.

The radius of sphere A was tripled to form sphere B.

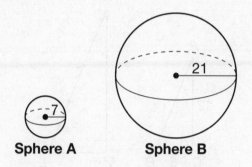

Sphere A   **Sphere B**

1. How does the surface area of sphere B compare to the surface area of sphere A?

   A. It is 3 times greater.

   B. It is 6 times greater.

   C. It is 9 times greater.

   D. It is 27 times greater.

2. How does the volume of sphere B compare to the volume of sphere A?

   A. It is 3 times greater.

   B. It is 6 times greater.

   C. It is 9 times greater.

   D. It is 27 times greater.

3. The diameter of a sphere is doubled. What will happen to the volume of the sphere?

   A. It will be twice the original volume.

   B. It will be 4 times the original volume.

   C. It will be 8 times the original volume.

   D. It will be 16 times the original volume.

4. The diameter of a sphere is multiplied by a factor of 6 to form a larger sphere. What will happen to the surface area and volume of the sphere?

   A. The surface area will become 36 times greater and the volume will become 216 times greater.

   B. The surface area will become 216 times greater and the volume will become 36 times greater.

   C. The surface area and volume will each become 36 times greater.

   D. The surface area and volume will each become 216 times greater.

5. The radius of sphere A was multiplied by $\frac{1}{4}$ to form sphere B.

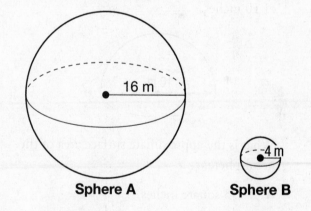

Sphere A   **Sphere B**

How does the surface area of sphere B compare to the surface area of sphere A?

   A. It is $\frac{1}{64}$ of the surface area of sphere A.

   B. It is $\frac{1}{16}$ of the surface area of sphere A.

   C. It is $\frac{1}{4}$ of the surface area of sphere A.

   D. It is 4 times the surface area of sphere A.

1. △*ABC* is shown below.

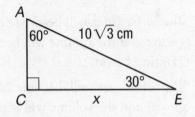

What is the missing length, *x*?

A. 5 cm

B. 5√3 cm

C. 15 cm

D. 15√3 cm

2. The hemisphere shown below has a diameter of 10 inches.

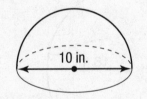

What is the approximate surface area of the hemisphere?

A. 393 square inches

B. 236 square inches

C. 157 square inches

D. 79 square inches

Use these similar triangles for questions 3 and 4.

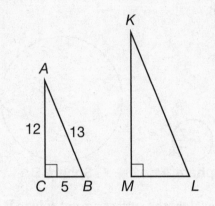

3. Which of the following must be true?

A. sin *C* = tan *L*

B. sin *C* = tan *M*

C. tan *B* = tan *K*

D. tan *B* = tan *L*

4. If sin $A = \frac{5}{13}$, then which of the following must also be true?

A. cos $L = \frac{5}{13}$

B. sin $M = \frac{5}{13}$

C. cos $K = \frac{5}{13}$

D. sin $L = \frac{5}{13}$

5. Line segment *PC* is tangent to circle *O* at point *C*, and $\overline{PA}$ is a secant.

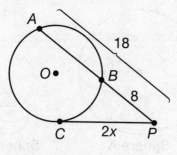

What is the value of *x*?

A. $2\sqrt{5}$

B. 6

C. $6\sqrt{12}$

D. 10

6. Circle *A* is shown below.

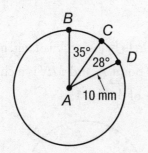

What is the approximate length of $\overset{\frown}{BD}$?

A. 55 mm

B. 11 mm

C. 6.1 mm

D. 4.9 mm

7. Mr. Reilly is building a wheelchair ramp from the ground to the front door of a house. The front door is 24 inches above the ground. The angle between the ground and the ramp will be 4.5°. What will be the approximate horizontal distance between the base of the house below the front door and the end of the ramp?

A. 2 in.   **C.** 274 in.

B. 25 in.   **D.** 305 in.

8. The length of the diagonal of a television screen tells you its size. An electronics store sells a special square television, shown below. The square with the darker shading represents the screen.

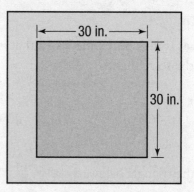

What is the approximate size of the screen, to the nearest inch?

A. 15 in.   **C.** 52 in.

B. 42 in.   **D.** 60 in.

9. The surface area of a sphere is 36π m². What is the volume of the sphere?

A. 3π m³

B. 12π m³

C. 36π m³

D. 122π m³

10. If the diameter of a sphere is multiplied by a factor of 5, what will happen to the volume of the sphere?

   A. It will be $\frac{1}{5}$ the original volume.

   B. It will be 5 times the original volume.

   C. It will be 25 times the original volume.

   D. It will be 125 times the original volume.

11. A searchlight is used as a part of a security system. The reach of the beam is 100 yards and it rotates at an angle of 120°, as shown below.

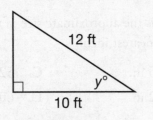

What is the approximate area that is covered by the searchlight?

   A. 12,560 yd²   **C.** 1,744 yd²

   B. 10,467 yd²   **D.** 209 yd²

12. In the triangle below, $\cos y° = \frac{10}{12}$.

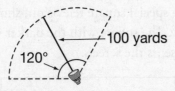

Which of the following must also be true?

   A. $\sin 90° = \frac{10}{12}$

   B. $\sin y° = \frac{10}{12}$

   C. $\sin (90 - y)° = \frac{10}{12}$

   D. $\cos (90 - y)° = \frac{10}{12}$

13. The radius of sphere A was multiplied by $\frac{1}{3}$ to form sphere B.

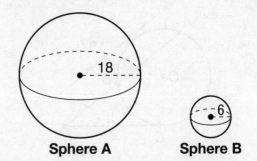

Sphere A   **Sphere B**

How does the surface area of sphere B compare to the surface area of sphere A?

   A. It is $\frac{1}{3}$ of the surface area of sphere A.

   B. It is $\frac{1}{6}$ of the surface area of sphere A.

   C. It is $\frac{1}{9}$ of the surface area of sphere A.

   D. It is $\frac{1}{27}$ of the surface area of sphere A.

14. In the circle below, *PN* is tangent to the circle at point *N* and $\overline{MN}$ is a chord. The measure of $\overset{\frown}{MN}$ is 134°.

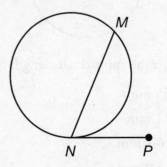

What is the measure of $\angle MNP$?

   A. 46°

   B. 67°

   C. 180°

   D. 268°

OPEN-ENDED QUESTIONS

15. In circle *O* below, $\overline{QR}$ is a diameter.

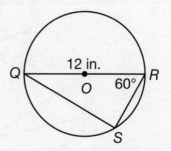

A. Triangle *QRS* is a right triangle. Use geometric theorems and/or properties to explain how you know this is true.

_____

_____

_____

_____

B. Use what you know about right triangles to determine the length of chord *QS*. Show your work or explain how you found your answer.

QS = _____

C. Now find the measure of $\overset{\frown}{QS}$. Explain how you found your answer.

$m\overset{\frown}{QS}$ = _____

_____

_____

_____

16. In the diagram below, $\overline{PG}$ and $\overline{PH}$ are secants drawn to the circle from point P. Line segments FH and EG are chords that have been drawn. Use the diagram below to answer each part of the question and prove that $r \cdot s = t \cdot u$.

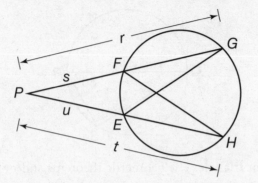

A. Use geometric theorems and/or properties to explain why the pairs of angles shown below are congruent.

$\angle PGE \cong \angle PHF$

$\angle GPE \cong \angle HPF$

_____

_____

_____

B. Use the angles from part A to explain why $\triangle PGE \sim \triangle PHF$.

_____

_____

_____

C. Show or explain why $r \cdot s = t \cdot u$.

D. In your own words, describe the theorem you just proved.

_____

_____

_____

CHAPTER 5
Data Analysis and Probability

32 Collecting Sample Data

MM2D1.a, MM2P3.a, MM2P3.b

A **population** is a group of individuals, items, or cases with something in common that someone may want to study. If you needed to study a large population, it would take too long to collect data about every member of the population. Instead, you can collect data from a **sample** of the population and use those data to make predictions about the larger population.

When sampling a population, it is important that the sample be representative of the whole population. In an **unbiased sample,** every member of the population has an equal chance of being part of the sample. The chance of any member being included in the sample is random.

A **biased sample** is not representative of the population. In a biased sample, some members of the population are more likely to be included in the sample than others.

In order to be representative, an unbiased sample must be large enough to show all the variation within the population. A sample that is too small is not likely to be representative.

EXAMPLE 1

Melinda wants to conduct a survey to determine the favorite hobbies of the students in her high school. Which sampling method will yield an unbiased sample?

Samples of the Student Population
Sample A: students in Melinda's art class
Sample B: students on the boys' and girls' soccer teams
Sample C: 10 boys from each of the freshman, sophomore, junior, and senior classes
Sample D: every tenth student who enters the school at the start of the day

STRATEGY   **Evaluate each sample to determine which is most representative of the population.**

STEP 1   What is the population Melinda wants to study?

The population is all students at her high school.

STEP 2   Consider sample A.

Sampling only students in Melinda's art class does not include students at her high school who are not in art class. Also, students enrolled in an art class may be more likely to have artistic hobbies.

This is a biased sample.

STEP 3   Consider sample B.

Sampling only students on soccer teams will not include students who do not play soccer. Also, players on a soccer team may be more likely to have athletic hobbies.

This is a biased sample.

STEP 4   Consider sample C.

Sampling only boys means no girls are included in the sample. Since the population of students at Melinda's school includes girls as well as boys, it is not a representative sample.

This is a biased sample.

STEP 5   Consider sample D.

Since every student enters the building at the start of the school day, randomly surveying every tenth student means all students have an equal chance of being part of the sample.

This is an unbiased sample. It is likely to be representative of the population.

SOLUTION   **Sample D will yield an unbiased sample.**

Sometimes, instead of studying one population, you want to collect data about two different populations and compare them.

EXAMPLE 2

Melinda completed her survey of a sample of students at her high school. The results showed that many students enjoy athletics. Melinda wants to conduct a second study. This time, she wants to compare two different populations: boys at her school and girls at her school.

What is one example of a question that Melinda could to ask? How could she collect good sample data from the two populations she wants to study?

STRATEGY   **Formulate a question. Then explain how Melinda could collect data about the two different populations.**

STEP 1   Formulate a question.

Melinda could ask, "How many minutes per week do you exercise?"

This is a good question to ask because students' answers will be in numbers of minutes. It is easier to compare two different samples when the data can be expressed numerically.

STEP 2   Describe one way Melinda could select her samples.

Since she wants to compare boys and girls, one sample should only be drawn from the population of boys and the other should only be drawn from the population of girls.

Melinda could obtain two alphabetical student lists: one with only males and the other with only females. She could then give a survey to every 8th name on each list and ask the students to return the survey to her. This should ensure that the samples are roughly the same size and are representative, since every student in each population has an equal chance of being selected.

SOLUTION   **One question Melinda might ask is, "How many minutes per week do you exercise?" To obtain a representative sample from each population at her school, she could select every 8th name from an alphabetical list of male students and every 8th name from an alphabetical list of female students.**

EXAMPLE 3

Melinda is planning to hand out surveys to a random sample of students. The students will return them to Melinda. What are the possible disadvantages to this method?

STRATEGY   **Consider why the survey method might not be reliable.**

STEP 1   Describe the disadvantages of using a take-home survey.

If Melinda is handing out a survey to be returned, some students may not take the time to return it. Melinda should pay attention to what percentage of surveys handed out are actually returned. This is called the response rate.

Another disadvantage is that students with a greater interest in athletics may be more likely to return the surveys because the topic is of interest to them. If that happens, her results may be biased.

STEP 2   Describe another method that might give a better response.

Melinda might get a better response if she surveys students face to face. However, if her samples are very large, this may not be practical.

SOLUTION   **One disadvantage is that not all students sampled will return the survey. If only a few students return the survey, the results will be biased. If her samples are not very large, she could instead interview students face to face.**

Duplicating any part of this book is prohibited by law.

COACHED EXAMPLE

Suppose your math teacher assigned a math project asking you to go out and collect data. What is one question you would ask? Identify two different populations you could study and describe how you would choose your samples.

THINKING IT THROUGH

Think of a topic that interests you.

I would be interested in finding out _____.

Identify two populations you could study.

I could study _____ and _____.

In an unbiased sample every member of the population has a(n) _____ chance of being part of the sample.

How would you collect unbiased samples from those populations?

_____

_____

You will probably ask more than one question during your study. What is the first question you would pose?

I would ask _____.

Will you ask your questions using a written survey, an online survey, a telephone survey, a face-to-face survey, or another method? _____

Briefly summarize your study on the lines below.

_____

_____

_____

Lesson Practice

Choose the correct answer.

1. Nicole is trying to determine the favorite food of students in her school. Which sample below is the least biased?

   A. a sample consisting of only Nicole's friends

   B. a sample consisting of every twentieth student to leave the school building at the end of the day

   C. a sample consisting of students living in Nicole's neighborhood

   D. a sample consisting of students in Nicole's mathematics class

2. Keyshon is collecting data to discover the average number of books that high-school boys read each week in his town. Which sample below would be best for him to use?

   A. a sample consisting of every tenth boy from an alphabetical listing of all students in his school only

   B. a sample of 50 randomly-selected boys from each of the high schools in his town

   C. a sample of 50 randomly-selected sophomores from each of the high schools in his town

   D. a sample of randomly-selected high-school boys who play on baseball teams in the town

Use this information for questions 3 and 4.

At Evan's school, an election is being held for school president. Evan wants to find out for whom most students at his school plan to vote.

3. Evan wants to compare two or more different populations at his school. Which would **not** be a good choice for the populations?

   A. two populations: the population of students at his school and the population of teachers at his school

   B. two populations: the population of male students at his school and the population of female students at his school

   C. two populations: the population of students in grades 9 and 10 and the population of students in grades 11 and 12

   D. four populations: the population of students in each of the four grades (9, 10, 11, and 12) at his school

4. Evan is trying to decide if he should interview students in person or use an online survey. Which is **not** a factor he needs to consider?

   A. Surveying students in person takes more time than using an online survey.

   B. He may not get a good response from an online survey because students may not take the time to complete it.

   C. There is no way to tally results using an online survey.

   D. Students without home computers may be less likely to complete an online survey.

5. Tamara is gathering data on the average weights of male and female dogs in her neighborhood. Which of the following is a biased sample?

   A. two samples consisting of every fourth male dog and every fourth female dog to visit the local vet's office one week

   B. two samples consisting of the male and female dogs living in every third house in Tamara's neighborhood

   C. two samples consisting of every 10th dog from a list of all male dogs registered in her neighborhood and every 10th dog from a list of all female dogs registered in her neighborhood

   D. two samples consisting of all of Tamara's male dogs and all of Tamara's female dogs

6. A cookie factory supervisor wants to compare how well four different machines work. One day, he tests every 30th chocolate chip cookie produced by each machine to see if it meets the company's requirements or not. Which best describes the population or populations he wants to study?

   A. all the chocolate chip cookies produced by only one of the machines

   B. all the chocolate chip cookies produced by each of the four machines

   C. all the oatmeal raisin cookies produced by each of the four machines

   D. all the cookies he selects for his study (every 30th cookie from each machine)

Use this information for questions 7 and 8.

A restaurant owner wants to add one kind of soup to his menu, but is unsure of which kind of soup customers would be most likely to buy. He wants to survey both male and female customers to find out.

7. Which question is most likely to yield the most helpful results?

   A. Do you ever eat soup?

   B. What is your favorite soup recipe?

   C. For lunch, are you more likely to order a cup of soup or a bowl of soup?

   D. Which of these three soups would you be most likely to order: chicken noodle soup, tomato soup, or vegetable soup?

8. Which two samples below would be best for him to use?

   A. one sample consisting of every fifth male customer who comes into the store next Monday and another sample consisting of every fifth female customer who comes into the store on that same day

   B. one sample consisting of every fifth male customer who comes into the store next Tuesday for breakfast and another sample consisting of every fifth female customer who come into the store for breakfast on that same day

   C. one sample consisting of 5 randomly selected regular customers who are male and another sample consisting of 5 randomly selected regular customers who are female

   D. one sample consisting of 30 randomly selected first-time customers who are male and another sample consisting of 30 randomly selected first-time customers who are female

33 Mean and Standard Deviation

MM2D1.b, MM2D1.c, MM2P1.c

After you collect numerical data, you will need to analyze it. You can start by looking at where the center of the data lies. One way to do this is to find the **mean** of a data set.

The mean of a data set is equal to the sum of the terms in the data set divided by the total number of terms. The symbol $\bar{x}$ is used to represent the mean of a sample.

$$\text{mean} = \bar{x} = \frac{\text{sum of terms}}{\text{number of terms}}$$

The mean can also be represented by the formula $\dfrac{\sum\limits_{i=1}^{n} x_i}{N}$, where N is the number of data points and x_i is the ith data point.

EXAMPLE 1

Students in Mr. Tyler's biology class and his horticulture class both started growing bean plants on the same day. Ten plants were randomly selected from each class and their heights, in centimeters, were recorded below.

Plant Heights (in centimeters)

Horticulture Class	10	14	11	12	10	13	13	12	13	12
Biology Class	8	15	10	8	16	16	10	14	9	14

Find the mean plant height for each sample.

STRATEGY Use the formula for finding the mean of a data set.

STEP 1 Find the mean of the data in the horticulture class sample.

$$\bar{x} = \frac{\text{sum of terms}}{\text{number of terms}}$$

$$= \frac{10 + 14 + 11 + 12 + 10 + 13 + 13 + 12 + 13 + 12}{10} = \frac{120}{10} = 12$$

STEP 2 Find the mean of the data in the biology class sample.

$$\bar{x} = \frac{\text{sum of terms}}{\text{number of terms}}$$

$$= \frac{8 + 15 + 10 + 8 + 16 + 16 + 10 + 14 + 9 + 14}{10} = \frac{120}{10} = 12$$

SOLUTION **The mean is 12 for both samples.**

EXAMPLE 2

The means for the samples in Example 1 are identical. Does that indicate that the spread of the data in both classes is the same?

STRATEGY   **Make a line plot to help you look at the data visually. Compare the plots.**

STEP 1   Make a line plot for the two samples.

Horticulture Class
Plant Heights (in cm)

```
              X   X
      X       X   X
      X   X   X   X   X
    ←─┼───┼───┼───┼───┼──→
     10  11  12  13  14
```

Biology Class
Plant Heights (in cm)

```
      X       X                   X       X
      X   X   X                   X   X   X
    ←─┼───┼───┼───┼───┼───┼───┼───┼───┼──→
      8   9  10  11  12  13  14  15  16
```

STEP 2   Compare the two plots.

Even though the means are identical, the line plots show that the two data sets are different.

The data for the plants in the horticulture class cluster near the center, 12.

The data for the plants in the biology class are much more spread out. They vary more from the mean.

SOLUTION   **The means are the same, but the spreads of the data for the two data sets are very different.**

As you discovered in Example 2, it is also important to look at how much the data varies from the mean. One way to do this is to find measures of variability. For example, you can determine how much each data point varies, or deviates, from the mean by subtracting $x_i - \bar{x}$. Because some deviations from the mean will be positive and some will be negative, square each deviation so each is a positive number. You can average those squared deviations to find a measure of variability called the **variance**. The symbol σ^2 represents the variance of a population and the symbol S^2 represents the variance of a sample.

The formula for finding the variance of a sample is $\dfrac{\sum\limits_{i=1}^{N} (x_i - \bar{x})^2}{N - 1}$, where N is the number of data points, $\bar{x}$ represents the mean value of the data set, and x_i is the ith data point.

The formula for finding the variance of a population is $\dfrac{\sum\limits_{i=1}^{N} (x_i - \bar{x})^2}{N}$, where N is the number of data points, $\bar{x}$ represents the mean value of the data set, and x_i is the ith data point.

You can take the square root of the variance to find the **standard deviation**, another measure of variability in a data set. The symbol σ stands for the population standard deviation, and S stands for the sample standard deviation.

The formulas for finding standard deviations are shown below.

Sample Standard Deviation	Population Standard Deviation
$S = \sqrt{\dfrac{\sum\limits_{i=1}^{N}(x_i - \bar{x})^2}{N-1}}$	$\sigma = \sqrt{\dfrac{\sum\limits_{i=1}^{N}(x_i - \bar{x})^2}{N}}$

In these formulas, N represents the number of data points, x_i is the ith data point, and $\bar{x}$ represents the mean of the data set.

Examples 3 and 4 show how to find standard deviations using two different methods—using a formula and using a graphing calculator.

EXAMPLE 3

Use a formula to find the standard deviation of the data for the horticulture class.

Plant Heights (in centimeters)

Horticulture	10	14	11	12	10	13	13	12	13	12

STRATEGY Subtract each length from the mean length, 12, and square the differences. Then use the correct formula to find the standard deviation.

STEP 1 Which formula should you use?

The data only includes a *sample* of the heights of plants grown by students in the class. So, use the formula for finding the *sample* standard deviation.

STEP 2 What do you need to do first, according to the formula?

First, we need to calculate $\sum\limits_{i=1}^{N}(x_i - \bar{x})^2$.

The expression $x_i - \bar{x}$ tells us to subtract the mean from each data point.

Then, we need to square each of those deviations: $(x_i - \bar{x})^2$

The symbol $\sum$ tells us to find the sum of all of those squared values.

STEP 3   Find the sum of the squared deviations.

In Example 1, you found the mean: 12. So, $\bar{x} = 12$.

Data value (x_i)	Deviation ($x_i - \bar{x}$)	$(x_i - \bar{x})^2$
10	$10 - 12 = -2$	$(-2)^2 = 4$
14	$14 - 12 = 2$	$(2)^2 = 4$
11	$11 - 12 = -1$	$(-1)^2 = 1$
12	$12 - 12 = 0$	$(0)^2 = 0$
10	$10 - 12 = -2$	$(-2)^2 = 4$
13	$13 - 12 = 1$	$(1)^2 = 1$
13	$13 - 12 = 1$	$(1)^2 = 1$
12	$12 - 12 = 0$	$(0)^2 = 0$
13	$13 - 12 = 1$	$(1)^2 = 1$
12	$12 - 12 = 0$	$(0)^2 = 0$

Find the sum of the squared deviations (the numbers in the last column):

$$\sum_{i=1}^{N}(x_i - \bar{x})^2 = 4 + 4 + 1 + 0 + 4 + 1 + 1 + 0 + 1 + 0 = 16$$

STEP 4   Calculate the standard deviation, using the formula.

The sample size, N, is 10. You know that the sum of the squared deviations is 16.

$$S = \sqrt{\frac{\sum_{i=1}^{N}(x_i - \bar{x})^2}{N - 1}}$$

$$= \sqrt{\frac{16}{10 - 1}}$$

$$= \sqrt{\frac{16}{9}}$$

$$= \sqrt{1.\overline{7}} \quad \longleftarrow \quad 1.\overline{7} \text{ is the variance.}$$

$$= 1.\overline{3} \quad \longleftarrow \quad 1.\overline{3} \text{ is the standard deviation.}$$

SOLUTION   **The standard deviation is about 1.3 centimeters.**

Low standard deviations, like the one in Example 3, indicate that data are clustered together. High standard deviations indicate that data are more spread out and have greater variability.

EXAMPLE 4

Use your graphing calculator to find the standard deviation for the data for the biology class.

Plant Heights (in centimeters)

Biology	8	15	10	8	16	16	10	14	9	14

STRATEGY **Use a graphing calculator.**

STEP 1   Enter the data into the calculator.

Press STAT . Then select **1:Edit...**

This brings up three columns for listing data.
Enter the data for the class in list L1.

L₁	L₂	L₃
8	---------	---------
15		
10		
8		
16		
16		
10		
L1(1) = 8		

STEP 2   Find the standard deviation.

Press STAT .

Press ▶ to move to the **CALC** menu.

Then select **1:1-Var Stats** and press ENTER .

```
1–Var Stats
 x̄ =12
 Σx=120
 Σx²=1538
 Sx=3.299831646
 σx=3.130495168
↓n=10
■
```

The data only includes a *sample* of the lengths of plants grown by students in the class. So, use the sample standard deviation, *S*, not the population standard deviation, σ.

The standard deviation is about 3.3 centimeters.

SOLUTION   **The standard deviation is about 3.3 centimeters.**

The standard deviation for the biology class data set (3.3) is greater than the standard deviation for the horticulture class data set (1.3). So, the standard deviations show what we already discovered just by looking at line plots of the data in Example 2. Even though both samples have the same mean height, the sample from the biology class is more variable than the sample from the horticulture class.

Although in real life you will not often work with data from an entire population, the Coached Example gives you practice using the formula for finding the population standard deviation.

COACHED EXAMPLE

These are the ages of all 7 members of a running club: 18, 17, 18, 21, 20, 17, 22.

The mean age of the players is 19. Find the standard deviation.

THINKING IT THROUGH

Since the population is all the members of the running club, you will find the population standard deviation.

Complete the table below.

Data Value (x_i)	18	17	18	21	20	17	22
Data Value − Mean ($x_i - \bar{x}$)							
Square ($x_i - \bar{x}$)^2							

Now, add the squares.

$$\sum_{i=1}^{N} (x_i - \bar{x})^2 = \underline{\quad} + \underline{\quad} + \underline{\quad} + \underline{\quad} + \underline{\quad} + \underline{\quad} + \underline{\quad} = \underline{\quad}$$

There are _____ members in the club, so $N =$ _____.

The mean, $\bar{x}$, is given as 19.

Substitute those values into the formula and solve.

$$\sigma = \sqrt{\frac{\sum_{i=1}^{N} (x_i - \bar{x})^2}{N}}$$

$$\sigma = \sqrt{\frac{}{}} = \underline{\qquad\qquad}$$

Use your graphing calculator to check your answer.

List the data by entering it in list L$_1$, as you did in Example 4. (If there is already data in that column, move your cursor to "L$_1$" and hit enter to clear the list.)

Then press [STAT]. Move to the **CALC** menu and select **1:1-Var Stats**.

Read the population standard deviation. Does it match the value of σ you found above? _____

The standard deviation of the ages is approximately _____ years.

Lesson Practice

Choose the correct answer. Assume all data are drawn from samples, not populations.

Use this line plot for questions 1–3.

This line plot shows the ages of a sample of dancers in a contest.

Ages of a Sample of Dancers

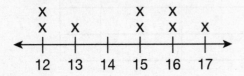

1. What is the mean age of the dancers?

   A. 14.5 years

   B. 14 years

   C. 13.5 years

   D. 11.6 years

2. What is the approximate variance of the dancers' ages?

   A. 1.35 years

   B. 2.92 years

   C. 3.61 years

   D. 3.9 years

3. What is the approximate standard deviation of the dancers' ages?

   A. 1.16 years

   B. 1.45 years

   C. 1.708 years

   D. 1.9 years

Use these data for questions 4 and 5.

The table below shows the heights in inches of samples of players taken from two basketball teams.

Heights of Players (in inches)

Eagles	68	70	72	72	73
Falcons	65	66	72	73	74

4. Which best describes the sample standard deviation for the Falcons?

   A. 2 inches

   B. 3.74 inches

   C. 4.18 inches

   D. 70 inches

5. Which statement accurately compares the data?

   A. The mean height is the same for both teams.

   B. The mean height is greater for the Falcons than for the Eagles.

   C. The sample standard deviation is the same for both teams.

   D. The data set for the Falcons is more variable than the data set for the Eagles.

6. The data below show the high temperatures in degrees Fahrenheit from August 31 to September 6 in Athens, Georgia, and in Portland, Maine.

High Temperatures (in °F)

Day	Athens	Portland
Sun.	90	80
Mon.	90	82
Tue.	88	82
Wed.	87	79
Thu.	88	88
Fri.	88	88
Sat.	91	74

Which statement accurately compares the means of the high temperatures in the samples above?

A. The mean for the Portland sample was about 7°F greater than the mean for the Athens sample.

B. The mean for the Athens sample was about 7°F greater than the mean for the Portland sample.

C. The mean for the Portland sample was about 3.4°F greater than the mean for the Athens sample.

D. The mean for the Athens sample was about 3.4°F greater than the mean for the Portland sample.

7. Ms. Moro wants to compare the history quiz scores of students in her first period class to those of students in her second and third period classes. The scores of ten students from each class were selected at random and are listed below.

Quiz Scores in Ms. Moro's Classes

1st Period	2nd Period	3rd Period
100	75	90
80	85	95
95	80	70
90	85	85
100	90	95
70	70	95
75	75	100
76	85	95
85	85	90
90	90	90

Which is **not** true of the variability of the sample data?

A. The standard deviation for the 2nd period class was about 6.7 points.

B. The standard deviation for the 3rd period class was about 8.3 points.

C. The sample from the 1st period class was the most variable of all the samples.

D. The sample from the 3rd period class was the least variable of all the samples.

34 Comparing Statistics from Samples to Corresponding Population Parameters

MM2D1.d

Often a population is too large to allow every member to be included in a study, so we collect data from a random sample of that population. If we find the mean and standard deviation of that sample, we are doing so to get an *estimate* of the mean and standard deviation of the entire population. We want to use our sample data to make **inferences** about the larger population, even though we can never know for certain what the entire population looks like.

If the sample you choose is representative of the larger population, then the statistics you collect about your sample are probably close to what they would be for the actual population. They are not exact, however. The means will vary from sample to sample. In general, as the size of a sample increases, the degree of variance found among the sample means will decrease.

To get an even better estimate of the mean for a population, you can take several equal-sized, random, unbiased samples drawn from the same population. Then you can average the means of the different samples to get a better estimate of the **population mean**.

EXAMPLE 1

Ms. Miller makes formal dresses. She surveyed 10 different random samples of high school girls in her small town to determine what she should charge for a prom dress. Each sample included 9 high school girls. The line plot below shows the mean price suggested by the respondents in her 10 different samples. Estimate the population mean.

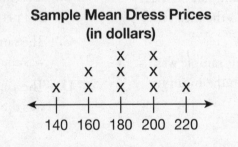

Sample Mean Dress Prices
(in dollars)

STRATEGY Find the average of the sample means in the line plot.

Find the mean of the sample means.

$140 + (160 \cdot 2) + (180 \cdot 3) + (200 \cdot 3) + 220 = 1,820$

There are 10 sample means.

$\bar{x} = \text{average of sample means} = \frac{1820}{10} = 182$

SOLUTION A good estimate of the population mean is $182.

Notice that the sample means given in Example 1 vary from one sample to the next. This is typical, since there is always some error with sampling. You can never be certain that a sample is exactly like the actual population. However, it is important to be sure that the means and standard deviations from different samples drawn from the same population do not vary too much.

EXAMPLE 2

For a class project, Marcus decides to investigate the distribution of heights of the 300 eleventh-grade boys at his school, Franklinton High School. He takes three randomly selected samples of 10 eleventh-grade boys and records their heights.

a. Find the mean and standard deviation of each sample below.

b. Will these samples provide good estimates of population mean and standard deviation?

Heights of Eleventh-Grade Boys (in inches)

Sample A	65	69	60	68	63	70	64	66	68	72
Sample B	68	76	73	69	77	73	75	70	73	75
Sample C	72	69	68	69	67	70	70	70	69	69

STRATEGY   Use your graphing calculator to find the mean and standard deviation of each sample. Then compare them.

STEP 1   Enter the data for each sample as list L_1 in your calculator and calculate the 1-variable statistics for that list.

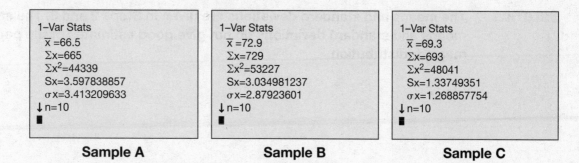

Sample A	Sample B	Sample C

STEP 2   Compare the means of the samples.

The range of a data set is the difference between the greatest and least values.

The range is 77 in. − 60 in. = 17 in. The means are 66.5 in., 72.9 in., and 69.3 in.

Given the range of 17 inches, those means are not close in value.

STEP 3   Compare the standard deviations.

The standard deviations are about 3.6 in., 3.0 in., and 1.3 in. Given the range, those standard deviations indicate that sample A has data that is spread out, sample C has data that is clustered together, and sample B is somewhere in the middle.

If you create histograms for the samples, you will see that this is true.

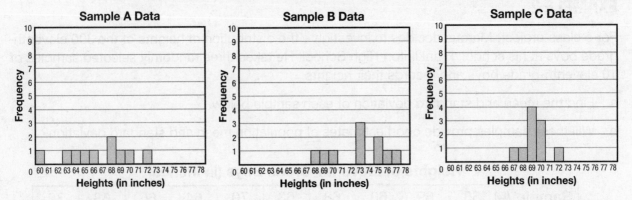

STEP 4   Determine if the samples will provide good estimates of the population mean and standard deviation.

The population is 300 boys and each sample had only 10 students. If small samples are taken from a large population, the samples are often biased. The sample means, sample standard deviations, and histograms above are very different.

If each sample were truly representative of the population, they would be more similar.

SOLUTION   **The means and standard deviations are given in Steps 2 and 3. The sample means and standard deviations do not give good estimates of the population mean or distribution.**

As you know, finding the mean of a data set tells you where the center is and finding the standard deviation gives you an idea of the spread of the data.

A **normal distribution** is a symmetrical, bell-shaped curve. It is a function of the mean and standard deviation of a data set. The maximum value of the curve is the mean. A good portion of the data is close to the mean. The curve below shows the percent of data that fall within a certain number of standard deviations from the mean.

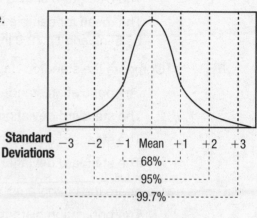

- About 68% lie within 1 standard deviation of the mean, in either direction.

- About 95% lie within 2 standard deviations of the mean, in either direction.

- About 99.7% lie within 3 standard deviations of the mean, in either direction.

If a population has a normal distribution, then you would expect unbiased, random samples to have the same distribution.

EXAMPLE 3

Marcus discovered that the heights of all 300 eleventh-grade boys at Franklinton High School are available in a computer database. He can now find the mean and standard deviation of the entire population. The histogram below shows the distribution of heights in that population. Compare the population distribution, the population mean, and the population standard deviation to what you learned about the distribution, means, and standard deviations of the samples in Example 2.

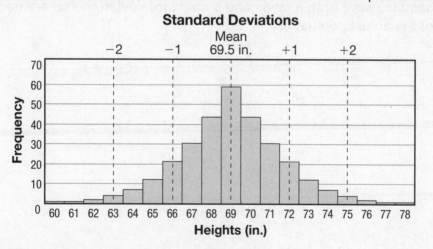

STRATEGY Compare the center and variability of the population to the measures you found for the sample data in Example 2.

STEP 1   Compare the means.

The histogram shows that the population mean is 69.5 inches.

The mean for sample C was close at 69.3 in, but the means for samples A, 66.5 in., and B, 72.9 in., were quite different.

STEP 2   Compare the standard deviations.

The population standard deviation is 3 inches.

The standard deviation for Sample A was more variable—3.6 in.

The standard deviation for sample B was close—3.0 in.

The standard deviation for sample C was less variable—1.3 in.

STEP 3   Compare the histograms.

The population histogram is bell-shaped, and it follows a normal distribution.

Only the histogram for sample C looks somewhat bell-shaped, although with so few data points, it is hard to tell.

STEP 4   What can you conclude about the sample means and sample standard deviations that Marcus found in Example 2?

Because the samples were so small and different from one another, the means and standard deviations of the samples are not likely to be good estimates of those measures for the population. Looking at the population distribution, we can see that this is true.

SOLUTION   **The population heights are normally distributed, whereas only one of Marcus's samples shows a distribution that looks like a bell-shaped curve. None of the samples have both a mean and a standard deviation that are good estimates of the actual population.**

COACHED EXAMPLE

Now that Marcus knows the heights of the entire population of eleventh-grade boys at his school, he decides to take eight more random samples. This time, he randomly selects much larger samples. The histogram below shows the mean heights, in inches, for Marcus's eight samples. Just by looking, you can tell that the means are close in value to the population mean shown in Example 3.

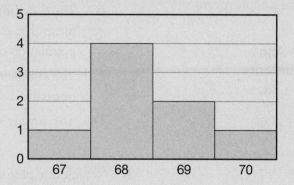

Compare the distribution of the sample means above to the distribution of the population from Example 3. Which is less variable? Explain.

THINKING IT THROUGH

Find the ranges for the population distribution and the mean distribution.

The population data ranges from _____ to _____. Subtract to find the range:

_____ − _____ = _____.

The sample means range from _____ to _____. Subtract to find the range:

_____ − _____ = _____.

The data for the _____ has a lesser range, so it is less variable.

You can also tell from looking at the histogram in Example 3 and the histogram above that

_____.

The distribution of the _____ is less variable that the distribution of the _____.

Lesson Practice

Choose the correct answer.

Use this information for questions 1 and 2.

There are 100 volunteers at a hospital. Lian selected 9 random samples of 10 volunteers each and asked them their ages. The sample means she found are shown below.

**Sample Mean Ages
of Hospital Volunteers**

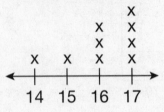

1. Which, if any, is a good estimate of the mean age of the entire population of volunteers?

   A. A good estimate is 14 years.

   B. A good estimate is 16 years.

   C. A good estimate is 18 years.

   D. The samples are biased, so the mean of the sample means will not be a good estimate of the mean age of the population.

2. Which statement about the distribution of the sample means is true?

   A. The distribution of the sample means has less variability than the population distribution.

   B. The distribution of the sample means has more variability than the population distribution.

   C. The sample means are normally distributed.

   D. The sample means are very variable.

3. Which line plot shows a normal distribution?

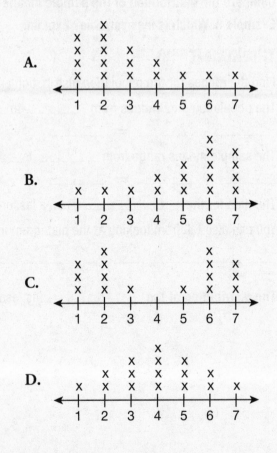

Use this information for questions 4 and 5.

A shipping company has a central location where packages are sorted. The director of the location collects the data shown below to learn more about the weights of the 1,000 packages that pass through the center each day.

Package Weights (in kilograms)

Sample A	Sample B	Sample C
4	2	5
3.5	2.5	4
2	4	2
2.5	3	2
3	4	3
3	2	3
4	2.5	4
5	4.5	5
3.5	5	3
3	4	3

4. If the samples are unbiased, what would be a good estimate for the mean of the packages that pass through the center each day?

   A. a mean of about 1 kilogram

   B. a mean of about 3.3 kilograms

   C. a mean of about 3.4 kilograms

   D. a mean of about 12.6 kilograms

5. Which of the following describes the best way for the director to collect unbiased samples?

   A. Choose 3 samples of 10 randomly-selected packages and record their weights.

   B. Choose 3 samples of 100 randomly-selected packages and record their weights.

   C. Choose 3 samples by selecting the first 10 packages that come into the sorting center one morning.

   D. Choose 3 samples by selecting the first 150 packages that come into the sorting center one morning.

6. Ricky collects data from 10 different samples and computes the sample means. He finds that his sample means vary slightly from one sample to the next. What does this indicate?

   A. If the sample means vary slightly, the samples must not be representative of the population.

   B. If the sample means vary slightly, the samples must be too small.

   C. If the sample means vary slightly and the samples are not biased, Ricky must have calculated the means incorrectly.

   D. Since sample means are only estimates of the population mean, a slight variation among the sample means is to be expected.

35 Gathering and Plotting Data

MM2D2.a, MM2D2.d

One way to determine if two different variables are related is to create a **scatter plot,** like the ones shown below.

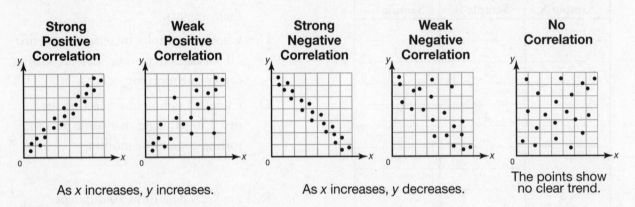

Strong Positive Correlation

Weak Positive Correlation

Strong Negative Correlation

Weak Negative Correlation

No Correlation

As *x* increases, *y* increases.

As *x* increases, *y* decreases.

The points show no clear trend.

Correlation describes the strength and direction of the relationship between two variables. A correlation can be either weak or strong. It can be either positive or negative. Two variables may also show no correlation.

EXAMPLE 1

Mr. Diaz wanted to see if students' study times were related to their test scores. The table below shows the time, in minutes, that a sample of students in his Spanish II class studied for a test and their test scores. Make a scatter plot of the data. Is there a correlation between the two variables? If so, describe it.

Study Time and Test Scores

Time (in minutes)	45	65	90	40	90	100	40	100	60	75
Test Score	70	85	95	65	90	95	75	100	80	90

STRATEGY Plot each ordered pair in the table on graph paper. Then decide if the plot shows a correlation.

STEP 1   Make a scatter plot of the data.

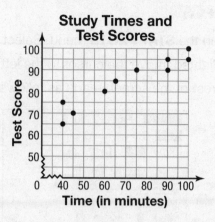

STEP 2   Describe the correlation, if any, that the scatter plot shows.

The plot shows a positive correlation.

In general, the longer a student studied, the higher he or she scored on the test.

SOLUTION   **The scatter plot in Step 1 shows that there is a positive correlation between the variables.**

You can also use your graphing calculator to create a scatter plot.

EXAMPLE 2

Plot the data from Example 1 on your graphing calculator.

STRATEGY   **Use your graphing calculator.**

STEP 1   Enter the data.

Press [STAT] . Then select **1:Edit...**

Enter each ordered pair in the table.

Enter the data showing study times in list L_1 and the data for test scores in list L_2.

L1	L2	L3
45	70	---------
65	85	
90	95	
40	65	
90	90	
100	95	
40	75	
L1(1)=45		

STEP 2   Set up the scatter plot.

Press [2nd] [Y=].

This brings up the **STAT PLOTS** menu. Select **1:Plot 1**.

If **Off** is highlighted, move the cursor to the left to highlight **On**. Then press [ENTER].

Be sure the rest of the screen reads as follows:

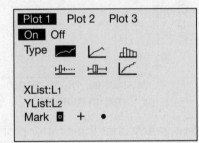

STEP 3   Graph the scatter plot.

Press [GRAPH].

You will need to adjust the window on your calculator to make it possible to see the entire plot.

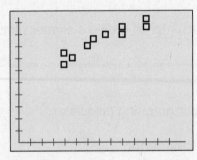

The plot on the calculator looks similar to the scatter plot in Example 1.

SOLUTION   **The scatter plot is shown in Step 3.**

The scatter plots in Examples 1 and 2 showed that there is a positive correlation between the time a student spent studying and his or her test score. However, this does not mean that the study time *causes* the test score. There may a third factor that you have not yet considered.

EXAMPLE 3

Mr. Diaz takes the same sample from the Spanish II class. This time, instead of comparing study times to test scores, he wanted to know if students' final grades in Spanish I were related to their scores on the Spanish II test. The scatter plot below shows his results.

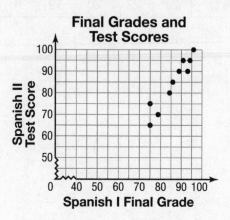

Describe the correlation shown by the graph. What does this tell you about the factors affecting students' test scores?

STRATEGY   **Describe the correlation. Consider how it affects what you discovered in Examples 1 and 2.**

STEP 1   Describe the correlation.

The plot shows a positive correlation between students' final grades in Spanish I and their Spanish II test scores.

STEP 2   Describe what this suggests about the factors affecting students' test scores.

Study time is not the only factor that affects students' test scores in Spanish II. Students' final grades in Spanish I are also positively correlated to their Spanish II test scores. This makes sense because what students learned in the previous year affects how well they will learn new material.

SOLUTION   **There is a positive correlation between students' final grades in Spanish I and their test scores in Spanish II. This shows that study time is not the only factor affecting students' test scores.**

COACHED EXAMPLE

Create a scatter plot for the data in the table on the grid below. Describe the correlation, if any, shown by the scatter plot.

Age of Car and Value

Age (in years)	0	1	2	3	4	5	6	7	8
Value (in thousands of dollars)	25	22	20	19	16	13	10	7	6

THINKING IT THROUGH

Create a scatter plot on the grid below.

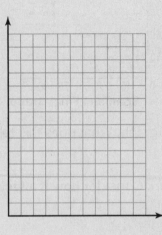

Determine if the scatter plot shows a positive correlation, a negative correlation, or no correlation.

The points tend to _____ from left to right, so the plot shows a _____ correlation.

Is the correlation weak or strong? The correlation is _____ because _____

_____

_____.

I created the scatter plot above and determined that it shows a _____ correlation between the two variables.

Lesson Practice

Choose the correct answer.

Use this information for questions 1 and 2.

The manager of a movie theater created the scatter plot below to help him determine if popcorn sales and beverage sales were related.

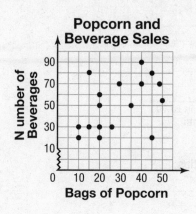

1. What type of correlation, if any, is shown by this scatter plot?

   A. strong positive correlation

   B. weak positive correlation

   C. weak negative correlation

   D. no correlation

2. Which of the following can you infer based on the scatter plot above?

   A. As the number of bags of popcorn sold increases, the number of beverages sold also tends to increase.

   B. As the number of bags of popcorn sold decreases, the number of beverages sold tends to increase.

   C. Buying bags of popcorn causes moviegoers to buy beverages.

   D. Every moviegoer who bought a bag of popcorn also bought a beverage.

3. Which scatter plot below shows a weak negative correlation?

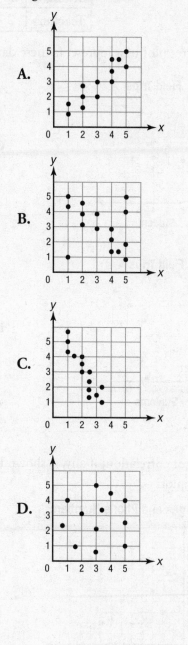

4. The table below shows the relationship between the number of students going on a field trip and the number of teachers accompanying them.

Field Trips

Students	28	38	45	48	57	65
Teachers	2	3	3	4	4	5

Which scatter plot best represents these data?

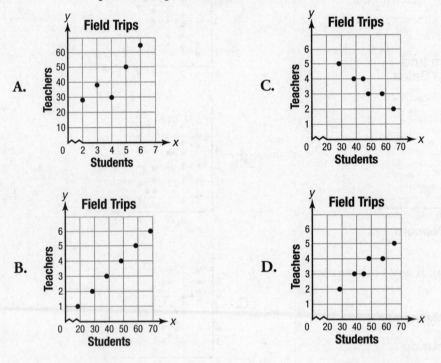

5. What type of correlation, if any, is shown by this scatter plot?

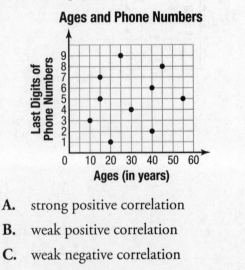

A. strong positive correlation

B. weak positive correlation

C. weak negative correlation

D. no correlation

6. What type of correlation, if any, is shown by this scatter plot?

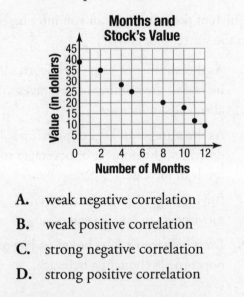

A. weak negative correlation

B. weak positive correlation

C. strong negative correlation

D. strong positive correlation

36 Linear Regression

MM2D2.a, MM2D2.b, MM2D2.c, MM2P4.a, MM2P4.c

As you learned in Lesson 35, plotting **bivariate data** in a scatter plot can help you determine if there is a relationship between the two variables. If there is a correlation between two variables in a scatter plot and the relationship appears to be linear, you can draw a **line of best fit** for the plot. A line of best fit helps you use a scatter plot to make inferences and predictions, and to draw conclusions about the data.

There are a number of ways to draw a line of best fit. One way is to "eyeball" the plot and draw a line that looks like the best model for the data. Once you draw the line, you can find an equation to express it algebraically. This gives you an **algebraic model** for the data.

EXAMPLE 1

The scatter plot below shows the lengths, in inches, and weights, in pounds, of a random sample of newborn infants. Draw a line of best fit for this scatter plot. Find its equation and use it to predict the weight of a newborn infant whose length is 17 inches.

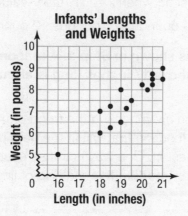

STRATEGY Use "eyeballing" to draw a line of best fit. Then make a prediction.

STEP 1 Draw a line of best fit with roughly the same number of points above it as below it.

There is no one correct line of best fit. Just be sure the line you draw seems like a good fit for the data.

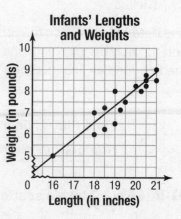

STEP 2   Determine the equation for your line.

The line goes through (16, 5) and (20.5, 8.5), so the slope is:

$$m = \frac{y_2 - y_1}{x_2 - x_1} = \frac{8.5 - 5}{20.5 - 16} = \frac{3.5}{4.5} \cdot \frac{2}{2} = \frac{7}{9}$$

You can then use the point (16, 5), the slope $\frac{7}{9}$, and the slope-intercept form to find the equation of the line.

$$y = mx + b$$

$$5 = \left(\frac{7}{9}\right)(16) + b$$

$$-\frac{67}{9} = b$$

So, the equation for the line is $y = \frac{7}{9}x - \frac{67}{9}$.

STEP 3   Predict the weight of an infant whose length is 17 inches.

Use the equation to make your prediction:

$$y = \frac{7}{9}(17) - \frac{67}{9} = \frac{119}{17} - \frac{67}{9} = \frac{52}{9} = 5\frac{7}{9}$$

1 pound = 16 ounces, so $\frac{7}{9}$ pound $\cdot$ 16 = $12\frac{4}{9} \approx 12$ ounces

So, a good prediction is that a 17-inch newborn baby will weigh about 5 pounds 12 ounces.

STEP 4   Use the line to check your answer.

On the line of best fit, when $x = 17$, the y-value is about $5\frac{3}{4}$.

$5\frac{3}{4}$ pounds = $5\frac{12}{16}$ pounds = 5 pounds 12 ounces

SOLUTION   **The line of best fit is shown in Step 1. A reasonable prediction for the weight of a newborn infant who is 17 inches long is about 5 pounds 12 ounces.**

When you draw a line of best fit, you are modeling the trend of the data with a linear function. With real-world data, there is usually no function that will fit the data perfectly. That is why we can use different methods to find a line of best fit. One way is to use eyeballing, as shown in Example 1. A second method is to use the **median-median line** method of linear regression.

EXAMPLE 2

The data below shows the time in minutes that Corinna played in each of 9 basketball games and the number of points she scored in each game. Make a scatter plot of the data. Then use the median-median line method to find a line of best fit.

Points Corinna Scored

Time Played (in minutes)	18	26	30	15	25	26	22	21	13
Number of Points	5	11	16	2	11	13	9	10	1

STRATEGY   Make a scatter plot. Then use the median-median line method.

STEP 1 Make a scatter plot of the data.

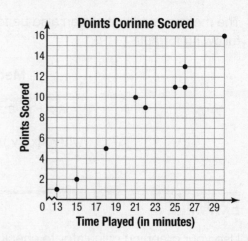

Points Corinne Scored

STEP 2 Order the data from least to greatest based on the *x*-values. Then break the data into three equal groups.

(13, 1), (15, 2), (18, 5)

(21, 10), (22, 9) (25, 11)

(26, 11), (26, 13), (30, 16)

STEP 3 Find the median of each group.

Group 1: the *x*-values are 13, 15, and 18, so the median *x*-value is 15.

The *y*-values are 1, 2, and 5, so the median *y*-value is 2.

The median for the first group is (15, 2).

Find the medians for the other groups.

Group 2: (21, 10), (22, 9), and (25, 11). Its median is (22, 10).

Group 3: (26, 11), (26, 13), and (30, 16). Its median is (26, 13).

STEP 4 Draw a dashed line through the first and third medians.

You can tell from the graph that the line has a slope of 1.

Calculate the equation for the line.

$$y = mx + b$$
$$2 = 1(15) + b$$
$$-13 = b$$
$$y = x - 13$$

STEP 5 Draw the median-median line.

The median-median line will have the same slope as the dashed line, but will be $\frac{1}{3}$ of the distance between the dashed line and the second median, (22, 10). For example, since (22, 9) is on the dashed line, then $\left(22, 9\frac{1}{3}\right)$ will be on the median-median line.

The slope will still be 1. Calculate the equation for the line.

$$y = mx + b$$
$$9\frac{1}{3} = 1(22) + b$$
$$-12\frac{2}{3} = b$$
$$y = x - 12\frac{2}{3} \text{ or } y = x - 12.\overline{6}$$

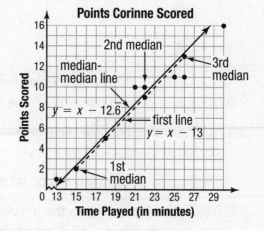

Points Corinne Scored

SOLUTION The median-median line is graphed under Step 4 and its equation is $y = x - 12\frac{2}{3}$ or $y = x - 12.\overline{6}$.

The median-median line can also be found by using your graphing calculator or by applying the following formula.

Median-Median Line Method

$$y = ax + b, a = \frac{y_3 - y_1}{x_3 - x_1}, b = \frac{y_1 + y_2 + y_3 - a(x_1 + x_2 + x_3)}{3}$$

where (x_1, y_1), (x_2, y_2), and (x_3, y_3) are the medians.

EXAMPLE 3

Use your graphing calculator to check your answer for Example 2. Then predict how many points Corinna would score if she played in a game for 20 minutes.

STRATEGY   **Use your graphing calculator.**

STEP 1   Enter the data in the table in Example 2 into lists L1 and L2 on your calculator.

STEP 2   Find the median-median line.

Press STAT .

Move to the **CALC** menu. Select **3:Med-Med**. Then press ENTER twice. The screen will look like this:

```
Med–Med
 y=ax+b
 a=1
 b=12.66666667
```

A median-median line is of the form $y = ax + b$. The screen shows that $a = 1$ and $b = -12.\overline{6}$. The equation for the line is $y = x - 12.\overline{6}$.

STEP 3   Predict how many points Corinna would score if she played for 20 minutes.

$$y = x - 12.\overline{6} = x - 12\tfrac{2}{3} = 20 - 12\tfrac{2}{3} = 7\tfrac{1}{3}$$

Since it is not possible to score $\frac{1}{3}$ point in basketball, a good prediction is 7 points.

SOLUTION   **According to the graphing calculator, the equation for the median-median line is $y = x - 12.\overline{6}$, which is the same equation found in Example 2. This equation can be used to predict that if Corinna played for 20 minutes, she would score about 7 points.**

Your calculator can find a regression line for a set of points, even if the line is not a good fit for the points. So, how do you know if your line is a good fit for the data? One way to do this is to eyeball the line and see if it fits the data points. A more precise way is to find the **correlation coefficient**, r.

Here are some facts that will help you interpret the correlation coefficient, r.

- The value of r is always in this range: $-1 \leq r \leq 1$.

- If r is close to 1, it shows a strong positive correlation.

- If r is close to -1, it shows a strong negative correlation.

- If $r = 0$, it shows no correlation.

You can find the correlation coefficient by programming your calculator to show its value every time you find a regression line. To do this:

1. Press 2nd 0. This pulls up the **CATALOG** menu.

2. Scroll down to **DiagnosticOn**. Then press ENTER twice.

Once you do this, the r value will be given every time you find a **linear regression**.

EXAMPLE 4

Angelo surveyed 10 randomly selected students to find out how many pages were in the last fiction book each read and how many days it took to finish it.

a. Use the least squares method of linear regression to find a line of best fit for the data.

b. If you used that line to predict the number of days it would take a student to read a 350-page book, how accurate do you think your prediction would be? Explain.

Pages in Book	243	250	300	199	320	385	284	201	400	315
Number of Days	6	7	4	2	5	12	10	9	7	11

STRATEGY   Use your graphing calculator to find the regression line.

STEP 1   Enter the data into lists L_1 and L_2 on your calculator.

Display the scatter plot.

Adjust the windows on your calculator to view the scatter plot.

STEP 2   Find the regression line.

Press [STAT].

Move to the **CALC** menu. Then select **4:LinReg(ax+b)**.

The next few steps instruct the calculator to input the equation for you as Y_1 on the Y= screen. These steps are optional, but they will save you time.

Press [VARS] [▶] **Y-VARS**.

Press **1** to select **1:Function...** and then **1** to select **1:Y_1**.

Now press [ENTER].

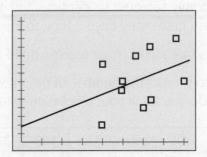

```
LinReg
  y=ax+b
  a=.0185040226
  b=1.939384664
  r²=.0151024481
  r=.3988764822
■
```

A regression line is of the form $y = ax + b$. The values of a and b on the screen are long, so round them when you write the equation for the line: $y = 0.019x + 1.94$.

Notice that this screen also gives you the value of the correlation coefficient, r.

STEP 3   Display the scatter plot and regression line.

If you press [Y=], you will see the equation for the line is already inputted for Y_1. That is because of the extra steps you took above.

Notice that when you do this, the full values of a and b are inputted.

STEP 4   How good a predictor will the line be?

The correlation coefficient, r, is about 0.4. That is not very close to 1, so there is a weak, positive correlation between the variables.

Looking at the scatter plot, you can also see that the line does not fit the points well.

So, if you used that line to predict the number of days it would take a student to read a 350-page book, your prediction would not be very accurate.

SOLUTION   **a. The regression line is shown under Step 3. The function $y = 0.019x + 1.94$ is a model for the data. b. The data are only weakly correlated, so if you used the line to make any predictions, they would not be very accurate.**

COACHED EXAMPLE

The manager of a large deli chose a random sample of sandwiches and recorded their prices and the number sold last week. Use the formula for finding the median-median line to find a line of best fit for these data. Draw it on the scatter plot below.

Price (in dollars)	Number of Sandwiches
4.00	68
5.50	55
3.50	85
8.00	22
5.50	64
7.00	28
6.00	56
5.00	59
8.00	32

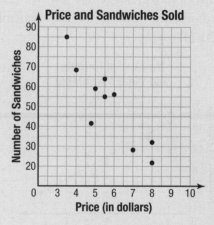

Price and Sandwiches Sold

THINKING IT THROUGH

Order the data from least to greatest based on the *x*-values, and break the data into three equal groups:

(___, ___), (___, ___), (___, ___) | (___, ___), (___, ___), (___, ___) | (___, ___), (___, ___), (___, ___)

Find the median of each group.

For the first group, the *x*-values are: _____, _____, and _____. The median *x*-value is _____.

The *y*-values are: _____, _____, and _____. The median *y*-value is _____.

For the second group, the *x*-values are: _____, _____, and _____. The median *x*-value is _____.

The *y*-values are: _____, _____, and _____. The median *y*-value is _____.

For the third group, the *x*-values are: _____, _____, and _____. The median *x*-value is _____.

The *y*-values are: _____, _____, and _____. The median *y*-value is _____.

Use the formula to find the median-median line. First, find the value of *a*.

$$a = \frac{y_3 - y_1}{x_3 - x_1} = \underline{\hspace{3cm}} = \underline{\hspace{3cm}}$$

Now, find the value of *b*: $b = \frac{y_1 + y_2 + y_3 - a(x_1 + x_2 + x_3)}{3} = \underline{\hspace{4cm}}$

$$b = \underline{\hspace{3cm}} = \underline{\hspace{3cm}}$$

Substitute those values into the equation $y = ax + b$ to find the equation of the median-median line:
$y = \underline{\hspace{3cm}}$

Use that equation to find two points on the median-median line.

Find one point: _____ Find a second point: _____

Graph the equation on the scatter plot. Label the two points you found and write the equation for the median-median line on the grid.

The line on the scatter plot and the equation $y = $ _____ are good models of the data.

Lesson Practice

Choose the correct answer.

1. The scatter plot compares the number of times a movie was rented last week to the number of weeks it has been available on DVD.

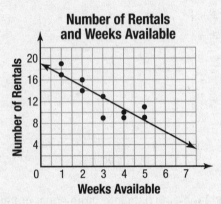

Number of Rentals and Weeks Available

Which is the best prediction of the number of times a video will be rented after it has been available for 7 weeks?

A. 7 times

B. 6 times

C. 5 times

D. 4 times

2. The correlation coefficient for two sets of data is $r = -0.43$. Which best describes the correlation between the two data sets?

A. weak negative correlation

B. weak positive correlation

C. strong negative correlation

D. almost no correlation

3. Mrs. Marcello sells televisions at an electronics store. She made a scatter plot to determine the relationship between the sizes and prices of a random sample of television sets. She then used eyeballing to draw a line of best fit, as shown below.

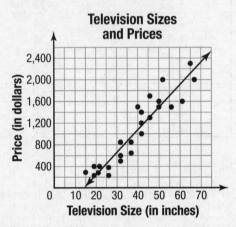

Television Sizes and Prices

Which is the best prediction of the cost of a 60-inch television set?

A. $1,600

B. $1,800

C. $1,900

D. $2,100

Use this table for questions 4 and 5.

The manager of a deli counter created this table. It shows the number of grams of saturated fat and the number of milligrams of cholesterol in a one-ounce serving of 9 different types of cheese.

Saturated Fat (in grams)	Cholesterol (in milligrams)
23.8	119
2.8	19
6.4	31
12.1	76
4.9	25
20.4	124
6	34
19.1	79
0.4	10

4. The manager will use the median-median line method to find a line of best fit for this graph. Which are **not** the coordinates of one of the three medians he must find?

   A. (2.8, 19)

   B. (6.4, 31)

   C. (19.1, 124)

   D. (20.4, 119)

5. Which equation best represents the median-median line?

   A. $y = 1.3x + 5.7$

   B. $y = 5.7x + 1.3$

   C. $y = 1.3x - 5.7$

   D. $y = 5.7x - 1.3$

Use the table below for questions 6–8.

Ms. Freeman is the manager of a small concert space. She wants to know if the price of a concert ticket affects the attendance at the concert. She chose a random sample of concerts from last year and recorded the ticket prices and attendance.

Ticket Price (in dollars)	Attendance
10	84
6	90
15	68
20	53
25	41
35	32
10	76
15	62
22	42
30	28

6. Which of the following equations best represents the regression line?

   A. $y = -2.3x + 100$

   B. $y = 2.3x - 100$

   C. $y = -2.3x + 0.93$

   D. $y = -2.3x - 0.96$

7. Which best describes the correlation between the two data sets?

   A. weak negative correlation

   B. strong positive correlation

   C. strong negative correlation

   D. almost no correlation

8. Based on your model, which is the best prediction of the attendance at a concert with a ticket price of $40?

   A. 40 people   C. 15 people

   B. 21 people   D. 8 people

37 Quadratic Regression

MM2D2.a, MM2D2.c, MM2P4.a, MM2P4.c

A linear function is not the only function model for a set of ordered pairs. Sometimes, a curve is a better fit. For example, a quadratic function may be a better model for some data than a linear function. There are several ways to find out if that is true.

One way is to eyeball the scatter plot to see if the data points resemble a line or a curve. Another way is to use the **method of finite differences** to determine if pairs of values form a linear or nonlinear relationship.

EXAMPLE 1

Consider the two sets of ordered pairs below. One table represents the perimeter of a rectangle with dimensions of x units and $(x + 4)$ units and the other represents its area.

Perimeter

x	$P(x)$
1	12
2	16
3	20
4	24
5	28
6	32

Area

x	$A(x)$
1	5
2	12
3	21
4	32
5	45
6	60

Which should be modeled by a linear function? Which should be modeled by a quadratic function?

STRATEGY   **Use the method of finite differences.**

STEP 1   Since the x-values are evenly spaced, find the differences between the output values for the first table of data points.

For example, $16 - 12 = 4$, so write 4 as the difference.

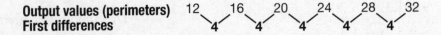

Output values (perimeters)   12   16   20   24   28   32
First differences   4   4   4   4   4

Since the first differences are constant, the data can be modeled with a linear function.

These first differences represent the slope of the linear function.

Note: If the x-values had not been evenly spaced, you would have needed to divide the differences of the y-values by the differences of the x-values to find the first differences, or the slopes.

STEP 2   Find the differences between the output values for the second table of data points.
Then find the second differences.

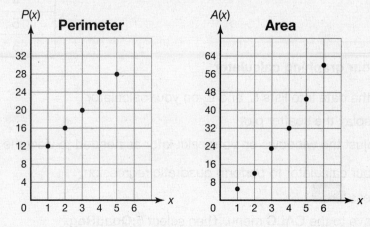

Output values (areas)   5   12   21   32   45   60
First differences   7   9   11   13   15
Second differences   2   2   2   2

Since the second differences are constant, the data can be modeled with a
quadratic function.

STEP 3   Graph the points and use eyeballing to check that your answers are reasonable.

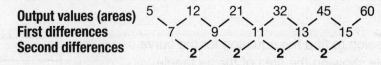

By eyeballing, you can see that a linear function perfectly fits the graph showing
the perimeter, P, and a quadratic function fits the graph showing the area, A.

SOLUTION   **A linear function is the best model for the first table of values. A quadratic
function is the best model for the second table of values.**

Example 1 shows that if the x-values in a table of values are evenly spaced and the first differences
between the y-values are constant, then the relationship is linear. In addition, if the second
differences between the y-values are constant, then the relationship is quadratic.

In Example 1, the second differences for the data showing the area of the rectangle could be
modeled perfectly by the quadratic function $y = x^2 + 4x$. In real life, there is usually no one
algebraic model that fits perfectly. **Curve fitting** means finding the curve that fits best.

In Example 2, you will use a graphing calculator to perform a **quadratic regression**.

EXAMPLE 2

Use quadratic regression to find the equation for the curve that best fits the table showing the area of the rectangle from Example 1.

Area

X	A(x)
1	5
2	12
3	21
4	32
5	45
6	60

STRATEGY **Use your graphing calculator.**

STEP 1   Enter the data into lists L_1 and L_2 on your calculator.

Display the scatter plot.

Adjust the windows on your calculator as needed to view the scatter plot.

STEP 2   Use your calculator to perform quadratic regression.

Press STAT .

Move to the **CALC** menu. Then select **5:QuadReg.**

The next few option steps instruct the calculator to input the equation for you as $Y_1 =$.

Press VARS  **Y-VARS**.

Press **1** to select **1:Function…** and then **1** to select **1:Y₁**.

Now press ENTER twice.

A **quadratic model** is of the form $y = ax^2 + bx + c$. So, this model is $A(x) = x^2 + 4x + 0$, or $y = x^2 + 4x$.

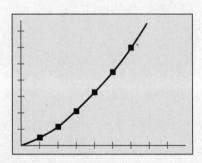

```
QuadReg
 y=ax2+bx+c
 a=1
 b=4
 c=0
 ■
```

STEP 3   Display the scatter plot and function model to check that your answer is reasonable.

If you press Y= , you will see the equation for the line is already input for Y_1. Actually, your calculator probably shows something that looks more complicated, such as $y_1 = .99999999999969x^2 + 4.0000000000022x + 0$. If you round these values, the equation is equal to $y = x^2 + 4x + 0$, or $y = x^2 + 4x$

SOLUTION   The equation of the quadratic model is $A(x) = x^2 + 4x$.

In Lesson 36, you learned that you can use a regression line to help make predictions. You can also use a best-fitting quadratic model to make predictions.

EXAMPLE 3

A company began producing an environmentally safe household cleaner in 2002. The table to the right shows the number of units of the product sold over the first 5 years it was on the market.

a. Find the best-fitting quadratic model for the sales of the product. Explain why a quadratic model is a better fit than a linear model.

b. Predict how many units the company will sell in 2012.

Year	Units Sold (in ten thousands)
2002 (0)	1
2003 (1)	1
2004 (2)	3
2005 (3)	6
2006 (4)	11
2007 (5)	18
2008 (6)	26

STRATEGY   **Use your graphing calculator.**

STEP 1   Enter the data into lists L_1 and L_2 on your calculator.

Let 2002 represent year 0, let 2003 represent year 1, and so on.

STEP 2   Use your calculator to perform quadratic regression.

Follow the same steps you used in Example 2. The equation for the model is $y = 0.82x^2 - 0.75x + 1$.

```
QuadReg
 y=ax²+bx+c
 a=.8214285714
 b=-.75
 c=1
■
```

STEP 3   Show that this quadratic model is better than a linear model.

Be sure that the equation for the quadratic model is entered as Y_1 on your calculator.

Then use linear regression to find the best-fitting regression line for the model. Enter the equation for that linear function as Y_2 on your calculator.

To do this, after you press **4:LinReg(ax+b)** on your calculator,

press  **Y-VARS**.

Then press **1** to select **1:Function...** and then **2** to select **2:Y_2**.

Display the scatter plot and both function models on your calculator.

You can see that the quadratic model is a better fit.

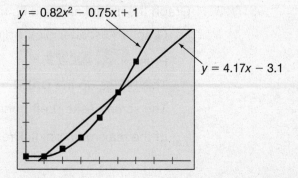

STEP 4 Use the model to predict the sales in 2012.

If 2008 represents year 6, then 2012 represents year 9. Substitute that value for x and solve for y.

$y = 0.82x^2 - 0.75x + 1 = (0.82)(9^2) - (0.75)(9) + 1 \approx 60.7$

This means that 60.7 ten thousands, or about 607,000, units will be sold.

SOLUTION **The equation of the quadratic model is $y = 0.82x^2 - 0.75x + 1$. It is a better fit than the linear model. The company will sell about 607,000 units in 2012.**

EXAMPLE 4

The manager of a large book store counts the number of books that are sold each hour since the store has opened. For example, the store opens at 8:00 A.M., so she will record the number of books sold from 8:00 A.M. to 9:00 A.M. as the number sold in the first hour the store is open. The table below shows some of her data.

Book Store Sales

Hours Since Opening	0	4	8	12	16
Number of Books	0	26	38	37	22

Write an equation for a function to model the data. Then use that function to predict the maximum number of books sold in an hour that day.

STRATEGY **Use your graphing calculator.**

STEP 1 Enter the data into lists L_1 and L_2 on your calculator.

STEP 2 Use your calculator to perform quadratic regression.

The equation for the model is $y = -0.42x^2 + 8.2x + 0.03$.

```
QuadReg
  y=ax²+bx+c
  a=-.4241071429
  b=8.160714286
  c=.0285714286

■
```

STEP 3 Graph the model and find its maximum.

Graph the scatter plot. Adjust the window as needed.

Press [2nd] [TRACE].

This brings up the **CALC** menu. Press **4** to select **4:maximum**.

The screen asks "Left bound?" Use the arrow keys to move the cursor to the left of the maximum point. Press [ENTER].

The screen asks "Right bound?" Use the arrow keys to move the cursor to the right of the maximum point. Press ENTER.

Then press ENTER again.

Remember, the maximum is the greatest y-value.

The calculator shows that the maximum is 39.3 when $x \approx 9.62$.

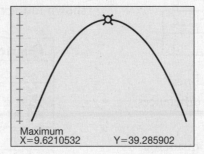

Maximum
X=9.6210532   Y=39.285902

Since a store cannot sell 0.3 of a book, predict 39 as the maximum.

SOLUTION   The equation of the quadratic model is $y = -0.42x^2 + 8.2x + 0.03$. A good prediction of the maximum number of books sold in any one hour is 39.

COACHED EXAMPLE

A projectile is shot upward from a point that is 5 feet above the ground. The table below shows the height of the projectile at various times.

Time (in seconds)	Height (in feet)
0	5
2	157
3	185
5	145
6	77

Write an equation for a quadratic function that models this situation. How good a fit is your model?

THINKING IT THROUGH

Use your graphing calculator. Enter the data in lists L1 and L2 of your calculator.

Use your calculator to perform quadratic regression. Follow the same steps you used in Example 2.

Your calculator shows that $a =$ _____, $b =$ _____ and $c =$ _____.

The equation for the quadratic model is $y =$ _____ $x^2 +$ _____ $x +$ _____.

The equation is _____ and the model is a _____ fit.

Lesson Practice

Choose the correct answer.

1. Which statement is true of the data points below?

x	0	1	2	3	4
y	15	12	9	6	3

   A. They can be modeled by a linear function, because the first differences are constant.

   B. They can be modeled by a quadratic function, because the first differences are constant.

   C. They can be modeled by a quadratic function, because the second differences are constant.

   D. No function is a good model for these data points.

2. An object was thrown from the top of a building. The table below shows the height of the object at various times.

Time (in seconds)	Height (in feet)
1	148
2	156
3	145
4	118
5	76

Using a best-fitting quadratic model, which is the best prediction of the time when the ball will be about 2 feet above the ground?

   A. 5.7 seconds

   B. 5.9 seconds

   C. 6.2 seconds

   D. 6.7 seconds

Use this table for questions 3 and 4.

The average quarterly stock prices of a new company for its first two years of business are shown in the table below.

Quarter	Price Per Share (in $)
1	2.00
2	8.00
3	12.50
4	15.50
5	17.00
6	17.00
7	16.00
8	13.00

3. Which equation shows the quadratic model that best fits these data?

   A. $y = 1.6x^2 + 5.6x$

   B. $y = 1.6x^2 - 5.6x$

   C. $y = -0.7x^2 + 8.1x + 5.4$

   D. $y = -0.7x^2 + 8.1x - 5.4$

4. If the trend continues, which is the best prediction of the price per share in Quarter 10?

   A. $1.00

   B. $6.00

   C. $9.00

   D. $10.00

Use the data for questions 5 and 6.

The table below shows how the annual costs of attending a college have changed from school year to school year.

Year (x)	Annual Cost in Dollars (y)
2002–2003	17,200
2003–2004	17,750
2004–2005	18,500
2005–2006	20,000
2006–2007	21,500
2007–2008	23,500
2008–2009	26,000

5. Which model best fits these data?

   A. $y = 190x^2 + 318x + 17{,}206$

   B. $y = 190x^2 - 318x + 17{,}200$

   C. $y = 1{,}460x + 16{,}253$

   D. $y = 1{,}460x^2 + 16{,}253x$

6. If the trend shown in the table continues, which school year would you expect to be the first to have an annual cost greater than $30,000?

   A. 2009–2010

   B. 2010–2011

   C. 2011–2012

   D. 2012–2013

Use these data for questions 7 and 8.

The braking distance for a car is a function of the speed at which it was traveling. The table below shows the speed, in miles per hour, and total stopping distance, in feet, for a particular car.

Speed (in mph)	Braking Distance (in ft)
10	17
20	43
30	82
40	132
50	194
60	265

7. Which quadratic model best fits these data?

   A. $y = 4.98x^2 - 52.1x$

   B. $y = 4.98x^2 + 52.1x$

   C. $y = 0.06x^2 - 1.02x + 0.7$

   D. $y = 0.06x^2 + 1.02x + 0.7$

8. Which is the best prediction of what the total stopping distance will be if the car is traveling 65 miles per hour?

   A. 349 feet

   B. 336 feet

   C. 321 feet

   D. 271 feet

1. Bella works at a day care center. She has noticed that there may be a relationship between how high the temperature is on a particular day and the number of bee stings that are reported that day. She made this scatter plot of her data.

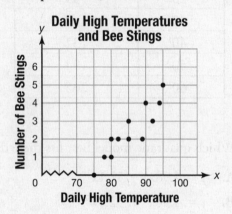

Which is a reasonable inference to make from these data?

A. There is a positive correlation between temperature and the number of bee stings that are reported that day.

B. There is a negative correlation between temperature and the number of bee stings that are reported that day.

C. There is no correlation between temperature and the number of bee stings that are reported that day.

D. Higher temperatures cause more bee stings.

2. There are 125 students in the Huntley High School Band. Tripp selected 10 random samples of 10 band members each and asked how many minutes they practice each night. The sample means he found are shown below.

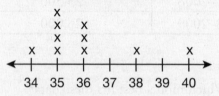

Which of the following statements is true?

A. The mean of the sample means is 35 minutes.

B. The mean of the sample means is 36 minutes, so that is a good estimate of the mean number of minutes that all band members practice.

C. There is no way to estimate the mean of the population because the samples are too small and are therefore biased.

D. The distribution of the sample means is probably more variable than the distribution of the population.

Use these data for questions 3 and 4.

For an experiment, Tamika leans over the roof of a building. She uses a machine to throw an object straight down at a speed of 48 feet per second. The table below shows the height of the object, in feet, at different times, in seconds, during the experiment.

Time (x) (in seconds)	0	0.5	1	1.5	2
Height (y) (in feet)	400	372	336	292	240

3. Which quadratic model best represents these data?

   A. $y = -52.8x^2 + 397$

   B. $y = 52.8x^2 + 397$

   C. $y = -16x^2 - 48x + 400$

   D. $y = -48x^2 + 16x + 400$

4. What will be the height of the object after 3.5 seconds have passed?

   A. 0 feet

   B. 36 feet

   C. 112 feet

   D. 180 feet

Use these data for questions 5 and 6.

The table below shows data for a random sample of employees at the XYZ Company. It shows the number of years of experience each has and their hourly wages.

Years of Experience	Hourly Wage (in dollars)
1	10.00
2	12.00
4	18.00
6	20.00
1	9.00
3	15.00
2	9.50
8	24.00
2	13.50
5	17.00
10	30.00

5. Which best represents the regression line for these data?

   A. $y = 2.2x + 7.5$

   B. $y = 2.2x - 7.5$

   C. $y = 2.2x + 0.96$

   D. $y = 2.2x^2 + 7.5x$

6. Using your model, which is the best prediction of the hourly wage for an employee with 15 years of experience?

   A. $25.00

   B. $35.00

   C. $40.00

   D. $50.00

Use these data for questions 7 and 8.

You want to know if the amount of rainfall your town gets affects how many umbrellas are sold at a local store. The table below shows the data you collected about these two variables.

Umbrella Sales and Rainfall

Rainfall (in inches)	2	3	3	4	5	5
Number of Umbrellas	12	11	14	15	16	18

7. Which scatter plot could you use to show these data?

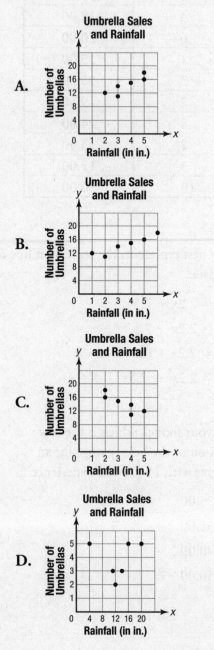

8. Use the median-median line method to find a line of best fit for these data. What is the equation for that line?

A. $y = \frac{2}{5} + \frac{2}{3}x$

B. $y = \frac{2}{5}x + \frac{2}{3}$

C. $y = \frac{5}{2} + \frac{14}{3}x$

D. $y = \frac{5}{2}x + \frac{14}{3}$

9. Anju wants to compare how well three different copy machines at her school work. One day, she will check the quality of every 50th photocopy made by each machine. Which best describes the population or populations she wants to study?

   A. all the photocopies produced by only one of the machines

   B. all the photocopies produced by each of the three copy machines

   C. all the photocopies she selects for her study (every 50th photocopy from each machine)

   D. all the defective photocopies she finds

Use these data for questions 10 and 11. Assume all data are drawn from samples, not populations.

The data below show the monthly rainfall, in millimeters, in Decatur, Georgia and in Seattle, Washington.

Monthly Rainfall (in millimeters)

Month	Decatur	Seattle
January	90	123
February	92	103
March	214	98
April	44	66
May	76	46
June	43	48
July	61	22
August	179	35
September	66	54
October	28	84
November	59	140
December	160	160

10. What is the approximate standard deviation of the amounts of rainfall for Decatur?

    A. 92.7 mm

    B. 83.3 mm

    C. 59.4 m

    D. 41.7 mm

11. Which statement accurately compares the amounts of rainfall in the samples in the table?

    A. The mean for the Seattle sample was about 11 millimeters less than the mean for the Decatur sample.

    B. The mean for the Decatur sample was about 11 millimeters less than the mean for the Seattle sample.

    C. The data appears to be clustered very close together for both data sets.

    D. The data for Decatur is less variable than the data for Seattle.

OPEN-ENDED QUESTION

12. A farmer is trying to determine how much fertilizer to use on his crop fields. He tried using different amounts of fertilizer, measured in pounds per acre. Then he recorded the yields for those fields, in bushels per acre (bu/acre). The table shows his data.

Fertilizer Used (lb/acre)	50	70	90	110	130	150	170
Yield (bu/acre)	37	59	75	84	86	81	70

A. Make a scatter plot of the data in the grid below.

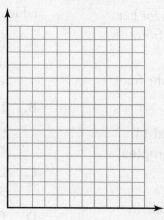

B. Which is the best model for these data points—a linear function or a quadratic function? Explain how you determined your answer.

_____

_____

_____

_____

C. Find the equation for the function that best models the farmer's data.

Equation: _____

13. Julia makes bags of homemade bread mix and sells them for a profit at fairs. The label on each bag says it contains 500 grams of mix. However, due to human error, the actual weight is sometimes slightly less or greater. To test how often this happens and to what degree, Julia randomly selects three samples of 10 bags and weighs each bag. She records the weights, in grams, in the table below.

Weights of Bags (in grams)

Sample A	500	498	497	495	504	501	502	500	499	505
Sample B	499	501	495	500	500	501	505	497	499	503
Sample C	496	497	502	497	505	503	498	503	499	502

A. Find the mean for each sample, to the nearest hundredth of a gram.

Sample A:　　mean: _____ grams

Sample B:　　mean: _____ grams

Sample C:　　mean: _____ grams

B. Based on Julia's unbiased samples, estimate the mean for the entire population—all the bags of homemade bread mix she sells. Explain how you chose your answer.

Population:　mean: _____ grams

_____

_____

_____

C. Assume that the weights of all the bags in the population are normally distributed. Based on that fact and your answer to part B, predict the weight ranges for 68% of the bags in the entire population. Explain how you determined your answer.

Sixty-eight percent of all bags in the population should have weights in the

range _____ grams to _____ grams.

_____

_____

_____

Glossary

30°-60°-90° right triangle a right triangle with two acute angles measuring 30° and 60°; in a 30°-60°-90° right triangle, the hypotenuse is twice as long as the shorter leg and the longer leg is $\sqrt{3}$ times as long as the shorter leg. (Lesson 24)

45°-45°-90° right triangle a right triangle with two acute angles measuring 45° each; In a 45°-45°-90° triangle (also known as an isosceles right triangle), the legs have equal lengths and the hypotenuse is $\sqrt{2}$ times as long as either leg. (Lesson 24)

absolute value the distance of a number from zero on the number line (Lesson 7)

adjacent arcs arcs of a circle that have exactly one point in common (Lesson 27)

algebraic model an equation representing real-world phenomena and/or a pattern shown in a graph (Lesson 36)

angle of depression the angle below a horizontal line formed when a point B is viewed from a higher point A (Lesson 26)

angle of elevation the angle above a horizontal line formed when a point A is viewed from a lower point B (Lesson 26)

arc a continuous portion of the circumference of a circle (Lesson 27)

arithmetic sequence a sequence in which a common difference is added to each term to obtain the next term (Lesson 17)

arithmetic series the indicated sum of the terms of an arithmetic sequence (Lesson 17)

asymptote a line that the graph of a relation approaches more and more closely as the value of a variable becomes extremely large or extremely small (Lesson 10)

axis of symmetry (of a graph) a line that passes through the vertex and divides a graph into two congruent halves that are mirror images of each other (Lesson 6)

biased sample a sample obtained by a method that favors some members of a population more than others; samples can be biased if the response rate or sample size is low, or if certain members of the population are systematically excluded from the sample (Lesson 32)

binomial a polynomial with exactly two terms (Lesson 19)

bivariate data data that involve two variables that may be related to each other (Lesson 36)

ceiling function a function whose value is determined by finding the least integer that is greater than or equal to the x-value being considered (Lesson 5)

central angle an angle formed by two radii of a circle, which has its vertex at the center of the circle (Lesson 27)

chord a segment whose endpoints lie on a circle (Lesson 27)

circumference the distance around a circle (Lesson 27)

common difference the common number added to obtain the next term in an arithmetic sequence (Lesson 17)

common ratio the common number by which each term in a geometric sequence is multiplied to obtain the next term (Lesson 14)

complementary angles two angles whose measures add to 90° (Lesson 25)

complex conjugates the product of the conjugate pair $a + bi$ and $a - bi$ is always $a^2 + b^2$ (Lesson 3)

complex number (*a* + *bi*) a number that has a real part, *a*, and a complex part, *bi* (Lesson 1)

composition (of functions) the act of combining two functions by substituting one function's formula in place of *x* in the other function's formula (Lesson 23)

compound interest interest earned on interest as well as on the original balance (Lesson 9)

conjugate pair two complex numbers in the forms *a* + *bi* and *a* − *bi* (Lesson 3)

conjunction a compound statement that uses the word *and* (Lesson 8)

constant interval in a function, an interval for which, as input values are increasing, output values remain the same (Lesson 6)

continuous function a function whose graph is an unbroken line or curve; the graph of a continuous function can be drawn without lifting one's pencil from a piece of paper (Lesson 6)

correlation a measure of the strength and direction of the linear relationship between two variables (Lesson 35)

correlation coefficient a number, *r*, that describes how closely the numbers in a scatter plot cluster around the linear regression line; the value of *r* is always greater than or equal to −1 and less than or equal to 1 (Lesson 36)

cosine (of an angle) the ratio of the length of the adjacent leg to the length of the hypotenuse (Lesson 25)

curve fitting the act of finding the curve that best fits a set of ordered pairs plotted on the coordinate plane (Lesson 37)

diameter a chord that passes through the center of a circle (Lesson 27)

discontinuous function a function whose graph includes one or more breaks, holes, or jumps (Lesson 6)

discriminant a part of the quadratic formula, specifically $b^2 - 4ac$ (Lesson 19)

disjunction a compound statement that uses the word *or* (Lesson 8)

distributive property a rule that states that multiplying a sum by a number is the same as multiplying each addend by the number and then adding the products (Lesson 3)

domain (of a function) the input values in a function (Lesson 5)

end behavior the appearance of a graph as it is followed farther and farther along in either direction (Lesson 10)

exponent the number of times a base is used as a factor (Lesson 1)

exponential function a function of the form $f(x) = a^x$, where the base *a* is a constant that is greater than 0 and the exponent *x* is any real number (Lesson 9)

extrema the maximum and minimum values of a function (Lesson 6)

f^{-1} "*f* inverse," notation indicating an inverse function (Lesson 21)

finite arithmetic series an arithmetic series that contains both the first term and the *n*th term in the series (Lesson 17)

floor function another name for a greatest integer function (Lesson 5)

function a set of ordered pairs in which each input value corresponds to exactly one output value (Lesson 5)

function notation a way of naming functions so they can be easily referenced (Lesson 5)

geometric sequence a sequence in which a common ratio is multiplied by each term to obtain the next term (Lesson 14)

greatest integer function a function whose value is determined by finding the greatest integer that is less than or equal to the *x*-value being considered (Lesson 5)

hemisphere half of a sphere; a three-dimensional figure with one curved surface and one circular base (Lesson 30)

horizontal line test a test in which one or more horizontal lines are drawn through the graph of a function; if any horizontal line crosses the graph of a function *f* in two or more points, then *f* is not a one-to-one function and the inverse of *f* is not a function (Lesson 22)

horizontal shift a transformation in which a graph or figure is slid to the left or the right on a coordinate plane (Lesson 13)

hypotenuse the longest side in a right triangle (Lesson 24)

imaginary number the square root of a negative number, written in the form *bi*, in which *b* represents a real number and *i* represents $\sqrt{-1}$ (Lesson 1)

inference (in statistical analysis) the process of arriving at a conclusion about an unknown distribution using data drawn from that distribution (Lesson 34)

inscribed angle an angle whose vertex is on a circle and whose sides contain chords of the circle (Lesson 27)

intercepted arc the arc formed by the endpoints of an inscribed angle (Lesson 27)

interval of decrease in a function, an interval for which, as input values are increasing, output values are decreasing (Lesson 6)

interval of increase in a function, an interval for which, as input values are increasing, output values are increasing (Lesson 6)

inverse of a function the relation that results from exchanging the input and output values of a function; the inverse of a one-to-one function *f* is a function and can be named as f^{-1}. (Lesson 21)

legs the two shorter sides of a right triangle (Lesson 24)

like terms terms that have the same variables raised to the same exponent or root (Lesson 2)

linear equation an equation that has a graph that is a straight line (Lesson 5)

linear regression a method of finding a line of best fit that minimizes the sum of the squared distance between each data point and the line; this method can be used to approximate a line of best fit for a set of data (Lesson 36)

line of best fit a line used to model the pattern in a set of ordered pairs (Lesson 36)

major arc an arc that is greater than a semicircle (Lesson 27)

maximum the point on a graph that has the greatest *y*- or *f*(*x*)-value (Lesson 6)

mean the sum of the terms in a set divided by the number of terms in the set (Lesson 33)

median-median line (method of linear regression) a method of linear regression in which all data values are split into three equal groups. The *x*-values are listed from least to greatest and the median *x*- and *y*-values for each group are determined. Those medians from least *x*-value to greatest, represent (x_1, y_1), (x_2, y_2), and (x_3, y_3). (Lesson 36)

method of finite differences a method used to determine if data points which have equally-spaced *x*-values could be best modeled by a linear function, a quadratic function, or another type of function (Lesson 37)

minimum the point on a graph that has the lowest *y*- or *f*(*x*)-value (Lesson 6)

minor arc an arc that is less than a semicircle (Lesson 27)

normal distribution describes a set of data whose distribution follows a mound-shaped curve (Lesson 34)

one-to-one property a property that states that for $a > 0$ and $a \neq 1$, $a^x = a^y$ if and only if $x = y$ (Lesson 11)

one-to-one function a function in which each output value corresponds to only one input value (Lesson 22)

piecewise function a function that can be represented by more than one equation, with each equation corresponding to a different part of the domain (Lesson 5)

point of discontinuity in a piecewise function, a point at which a graph becomes discontinuous because of a hole, gap, or jump in the graph (Lesson 6)

point of tangency the point at which a tangent line or tangent segment intersects a circle (Lesson 27)

polynomial the sum or difference of two or more unlike terms (Lesson 2)

population the entire set of cases or individuals being studied or considered (Lesson 32)

population mean the mean of a set of numbers that includes all members of the entire group being studied or considered (Lesson 34)

power the result of raising a base to an exponent (Lesson 1)

power function a function in the form $f(x) = x^a$, where a is a real number and $a \neq 0$ (Lesson 21)

quadratic equation a polynomial equation in which the greatest exponent to which the variable is raised is 2 (Lesson 18)

quadratic formula formula for finding the values of x for a quadratic equation in the form $ax^2 + bx + c = 0$ with $a \neq 0$; the formula is: $x = \dfrac{-b \pm \sqrt{b^2 - 4ac}}{2a}$. (Lesson 19)

quadratic function a function in which the greatest exponent to which the variable is raised is 2 (Lesson 15)

quadratic model the quadratic equation of a function used to model real-world phenomena and/or a pattern shown in a graph (Lesson 37)

quadratic regression a statistical method used to fit a quadratic function to a set of data (Lesson 37)

radius a segment with an endpoint on a circle and the other endpoint at the center of the circle (Lesson 27)

range (of a function) the output values of a function (Lesson 6)

real number any number on the number line; can be rational or irrational (Lesson 1)

reciprocals two numbers whose product is 1 (Lesson 4)

reflection a transformation in which a graph or figure is flipped across a line (Lesson 13)

right triangle a triangle which has one right angle (Lesson 24)

root (of an equation) any value of x that makes $f(x) = 0$ true (Lesson 18)

sample a subset of a population (Lesson 32)

scatter plot a graph of ordered pairs used to determine if two variables are related (Lesson 35)

secant (of a circle) a line or segment that contains a chord of a circle (Lesson 27)

sector a region of a circle with two radii and an arc of the circle as its boundaries (Lesson 29)

semicircle an arc of a circle whose endpoints are the endpoints of a diameter of the circle (Lesson 27)

shrink a transformation; a vertical shrink pushes the points of a graph toward the x-axis and a horizontal shrink pushes the points of a graph toward the y-axis (Lesson 13)

similar triangles two or more triangles that have the same shape but not necessarily the same size (Lesson 25)

sine (of an angle) the ratio of the length of the opposite leg to the length of the hypotenuse (Lesson 25)

slope a ratio that compares the change in the y-coordinates to the change in the x-coordinates (Lesson 5)

slope-intercept form the form $y = mx + b$, where m represents the slope and b represents the y-intercept, used to represent a line (Lesson 5)

square root one of the two equal factors of a number (Lesson 1)

square root principle the principle that states that if $u^2 = c$ and $c > 0$, then $u = \pm\sqrt{c}$. (Lesson 19)

standard deviation a measure of dispersion for a data set; the symbol σ stands for the population standard deviation and S stands for the sample standard deviation. (Lesson 33)

standard form (of a quadratic function) a quadratic function written in the form $f(x) = ax^2 + bx + c$, in which a, b, and c are real numbers and $a \neq 0$ (Lesson 15)

step function a piecewise function whose graph resembles a staircase (Lesson 5)

stretch a transformation; a vertical stretch pulls the points of a graph away from the x-axis and a horizontal stretch pulls the points of a graph away from the y-axis. (Lesson 13)

supplementary angles two angles whose measures add to 180° (Lesson 27)

tangent (of an angle) the ratio of the length of the opposite leg to the length of the adjacent leg (Lesson 25)

tangent (to a circle) a line or segment that intersects a circle in exactly one point (Lesson 27)

transformation an operation on a geometric figure or graph by which an image is created (Lesson 13)

trigonometric ratio a ratio that relates two side lengths of a right triangle to one of its angles (Lesson 25)

trigonometry the study of triangles (Lesson 25)

unbiased sample a sample obtained by a method in which one member of a population is no more likely to be included or favored than any other member (Lesson 32)

variance the average of the squared deviations from the mean; the symbol σ^2 represents the variance of a population and the symbol S^2 represents the variance of a sample (Lesson 33)

vertex the minimum or maximum point on the graph of an absolute value function or a quadratic function (Lesson 6)

vertex form (of a quadratic function) a quadratic function written in the form $f(x) = a(x - h)^2 + k$, where $a \neq 0$, and a, h, and k are constants; the vertex of a function written in this form is at (h, k) (Lesson 15)

vertical shift a transformation in which a graph or figure is slid up or down on a coordinate plane (Lesson 13)

***x*-intercept** the point at which a graph crosses the *x*-axis (Lesson 6)

***y*-intercept** the point at which a graph crosses the *y*-axis (Lesson 5)

zero (of a function) for a function {x, $f(x)$}, the value of x that makes $f(x) = 0$ (Lesson 6)

zero product property the property that states that if $ab = 0$, then $a = 0$ and/or $b = 0$ (Lesson 19)

Mathematics II Formula Sheet

Below are the formulas you may find useful as you work the problems. However, some of the formulas may not be used. You may refer to this page as you take the test.

Area

Rectangle/Parallelogram $A = bh$

Triangle $A = \frac{1}{2}bh$

Circle $A = \pi r^2$

Circumference

$C = \pi d$ $\pi \approx 3.14$

Volume

Rectangular Prism/Cylinder $V = Bh$

Pyramid/Cone $V = \frac{1}{3}Bh$

Sphere $V = \frac{4}{3}\pi r^3$

Surface Area

Rectangular Prism $SA = 2lw + 2wh + 2lh$

Cylinder $SA = 2\pi r^2 + 2\pi rh$

Sphere $SA = 4\pi r^2$

Trigonometric Relationships

$\sin(\theta) = \dfrac{\text{opp}}{\text{hyp}}; \cos(\theta) = \dfrac{\text{adj}}{\text{hyp}}; \tan(\theta) = \dfrac{\text{opp}}{\text{adj}}$

Quadratic Formula

$$x = \frac{-b \pm \sqrt{b^2 - 4ac}}{2a}$$

Standard Form $ax^2 + bx + c = y$

Vertex Form $a(x - h)^2 + k = y$

Mean Absolute Deviation

$$\frac{\sum\limits_{i=1}^{N} |x_i - \overline{x}|}{N}$$

the average of the absolute deviations from the mean for a set of data

Population Standard Deviation

$$\sigma = \sqrt{\frac{\sum\limits_{i=1}^{N} (x_i - \overline{x})^2}{N}}$$

Sample Standard Deviation

$$S = \sqrt{\frac{\sum\limits_{i=1}^{N} (x_i - \overline{x})^2}{N - 1}}$$

Special Right Triangles

45°–45°–90° Triangle

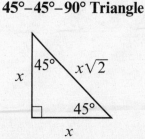

30°–60°–90° Triangle

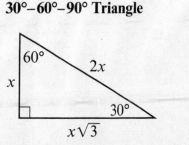

Notes

Notes

Notes

Notes